THE BLANDFORD GUIDE TO

TREES

OF THE
BRITISH COUNTRYSIDE

THE BLANDFORD GUIDE TO

TREES

OF THE
BRITISH COUNTRYSIDE

Alan Fairhurst and Eric Soothill

BLANDFORD PRESS
POOLE   DORSET

First published in the U.K. 1981 by Blandford Press
Link House, West Street,
Poole, Dorset, BH15 1LL

Copyright © 1981 Blandford Books Ltd

British Library Cataloguing in Publication Data

Fairhurst, Alan
  The Blandford guide to trees of the British
  countryside.
  1. Trees — Great Britain — Identification
  I. Title   II. Soothill, Eric
  582.160941   QK488

ISBN 0 7137 0938 3

Typeset in Monophoto Melior
by Oliver Burridge Filmsetting Ltd
and printed by South China
Printing Co. Hong Kong

Contents

Acknowledgements

The authors are grateful to the following people and organisations for the help they gave in the preparation of this book:
Norah Atherton; M. Baecker; Ron Barker; Bolton Museum; S. Bowstead; Jack Cooper; Alan Creaser; Dr Beti Evans; Forestry Commission, Gwydyr Uchaf, Llanwrst; D. G. Gooding; Charles Griffiths; Len and Pat Livermore; John Mashiter; National Trust, Bodnant; Mr and Mrs G. D. O'Brien; Parks Department, Rochdale; Neil Robinson; Peter Skidmore; Richard Soothill; Dr G. Taylor; Mike and Ann Thomas; Prof. D. H. Valentine; John C. Voysey, Forestry Commission, Kendal; The Rt. Hon. Lord Wakefield of Kendal; Ralph Walker; Dr Roy Watling, Royal Botanic Garden, Edinburgh; Mr Whewell, Wyresdale Park.
We are especially indebted to Dr E. M. Adcock of Bolton for reading the original manuscript and offering constructive criticism; also to Alan Brindle MSc., Entomologist to Manchester University Museum for his help with the lists of Associated Insects.
All the photographs in this book were taken by Eric Soothill with the exception of the Wayfaring Tree habit (Sdeuard C. Bisserot) and the Norway Spruce flowers (Robin Fletcher). Line illustrations are by Doreen Edmond.

Dedication

*This book is
dedicated to the memory
of the late W. Arthur Watson,
friend and fellow
naturalist.*

Foreword

When I first received notification of this book I must confess I groaned, 'not another book on how to identify our common trees and shrubs!'

Then I took a look at the proofs and the pictures, and was of course delighted. Not just another book but one well up to the standards we have come to expect from a Blandford Guide and one containing new and relevant detail.

To me a tree or shrub is a many splendoured thing purely from a down to earth botanist's point of view. It is of course much more than that: each one is a 'high rise building' for it provides habitats for an amazing variety of other plants and animals.

This book provides the budding naturalist with a key to some of the many doors in nature's own multi-storeyed real estate.

Check the identity of the tree or shrub (that's easy with the pictures and the text) and then begin to get to grips with the wonderful world of the mushrooms, toadstools and their kin and with the amazing diversity of the insects.

This book will be especially useful to the townbound naturalist. The majority of the trees and shrubs can be found growing within our urban areas and most descriptions include notes concerning their place or otherwise in the garden. Then the fun begins: I bet you didn't know one hundredth of the things you share your garden with!

Good gardening and good botanizing!

David Bellamy
Bedburn 1981

Introduction

By definition, trees are woody, perennial plants which increase in size year by year, as opposed to herbaceous plants which die back each autumn. The distinction between trees and shrubs is tenuous, retained more for convenience than for any botanical reason, and is normally considered to be that a tree is single stemmed from ground level and attains a height of over 6 m, whereas shrubs are multi-stemmed, ranging from 30 cm to 6 m in height. However, having said that, it is not in fact possible to categorise many species into trees or shrubs because the way a plant grows so often depends on its situation, the soil, climatic conditions and man's interference. For example, the Common Osier is normally coppiced to produce a small, round shrub, but if left alone and in a favourable, open spot it can grow into a tree up to 9 m high. For this reason we have made no distinction in this book between shrubs and trees, including species such as Gorse and Blackthorn.

Because trees increase in size annually and do not die back at the end of each growing season, they need a stem which increases in size and strength yearly to support the growing weight of the crown. They therefore develop a woody stem or trunk which increases in girth every year. The function of the trunk is two-fold: firstly it supports the crown of the tree, and secondly it acts as a transportation system connecting the roots to the leaves.

If a trunk or large branch is cut across, distinct areas of different colour and texture can be seen. By far the largest area is xylem—the wood—which lends the structural strength needed to support the tree. However, the wood is not only structural: it is made up of tubular cells through which water and mineral salts flow from the roots to the leaves. In mature trees, two types of wood can be seen in the cross-section: the dense heartwood forming the central column and the more open sapwood surrounding it. Heartwood is dead; it no longer functions as a conducting tissue and the cells are blocked and filled with waste substances which help to impart considerable strength to the trunk. It is usually darker in colour and considered to be of superior quality for use than the surrounding sapwood through part of which the sap still

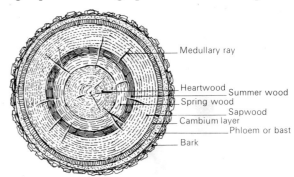

Medullary ray

Heartwood Summer wood
Spring wood
            Sapwood
Cambium layer
            Phloem or bast

Bark

rises. If a tree is damaged and water penetrates the trunk rotting away the heartwood, the tree still survives, although structurally weakened, for it is the outer layers which perform the vital functions.

The fibrous layer surrounding the xylem is the phloem or bast, made up of elements through which the organic compounds manufactured in the leaves are conducted to the growing parts of the tree. This is separated from the xylem by a single layer of cells—the cambium—which, when the tree is growing, divide rapidly to produce new xylem vessels on the inside and new phloem cells on the outside. The concentric rings in the wood which can be seen in the cross-section of a trunk or large branch are due to a definite rhythm in the activity of these cambial cells. In spring when the tree is growing most rapidly and, in the case of deciduous trees, putting out new foliage, the cambium produces wide xylem vessels which can conduct the large amounts of water necessary for growth. As the summer draws on, the growth rate declines and the xylem cells produced become progressively smaller, with thicker cell walls, built more for strength than for rapid sap flow. No wood is added in winter. It is this alternation of loose-textured spring wood and dense autumn wood that gives the annual concentric rings by which the age of a tree can be determined.

To allow for transverse conduction of materials in the wood, radiating medullary rays of thin-walled cells are produced and maintained by the cambium. As the trunk increases in girth, more medullary rays are produced in the outer wood. It is the annual rings and medullary rays which give the graining of timber valued for its decorative effect. As a protection against water loss, extremes of temperature and mechanical damage, the trunk is covered by a waterproof layer of dead cells—the bark. This is maintained and thickened by the cork cambium. However, the living tissue of the trunk must breathe and so the bark is not entirely airtight: to allow for the passage of gases in and out of the trunk there are small porous areas in the bark called lenticels. These can be seen as small elongated or rounded raised patches of a slightly different colour than the surrounding bark. The shape and colour of the lenticels are often characteristic of a particular species.

In this book we have concentrated on the bark as an important identification feature. The texture and colour of the bark develops throughout the life of a tree, usually becoming more fissured as the girth increases and the oldest layers of cork split. However, the direction in which it fissures, whether, for example, as in Sycamore, plates form and peel off, the shape of the lenticels, the thickness of the bark and the overall colour, are all characteristic and can act as a guide to the identification of a tree.

We do not propose to go into the subject of tree nutrition here; suffice to say that, as in all green plants, the leaves use energy from sunlight to convert carbon dioxide and water into carbohydrates via the process known as photosynthesis. This depends on the presence of chlorophyll, the green colouring matter of leaves, which is the vital factor in the absorption of the light energy. The carbohydrates produced in photosynthesis are conducted from the leaves throughout the tree via the phloem system and are used as the basic building blocks for growth. To provide energy for growth the carbohydrates are broken down using up oxygen absorbed from the atmosphere and releasing carbon dioxide.

The water and mineral salts used in photosynthesis are absorbed from the soil by rootlets and are conducted through the xylem to the leaves which may, for instance in the case of a mature Lime tree, be 45 m or more above ground level. This remarkable lift is achieved partly by root pressure and capillary action but is facilitated by transpiration —the active loss of water from the leaves. As water from the leaf cells evaporates through pores in the leaf surface known as stomata, water to replace it is drawn up in a continuous column from the roots.

In a large tree the amount of water lost through transpiration can be as much as 200–400 gallons per day. If one considers a large forest made up of hundreds of thousands of trees, each releasing this amount of water into the air, one can see that the effect of transpiration on the humidity of the atmosphere and therefore on the weather of the region must be considerable. Combine this with the effect on soil water and it can be seen that large scale deforestation such as is practised by man in many parts of the world, inevitably has devastating results on the ecology of an area with widespread flooding and erosion.

Control of transpiration is of vital importance to the tree if it is to maintain a balance of water throughout its tissues. On a short term basis control is achieved by opening and closing the stomata. If the sun is strong and water is evaporating from the leaves faster than it can be drawn up from the roots, special cells on either side of each stoma lose their turgidity and close the opening.

In temperate regions in winter the soil becomes cold, severely inhibiting water uptake by the roots of trees. Broad-leaved trees must drastically reduce the vast surface area that their leaves present to the atmosphere if they are to reduce water loss and maintain a balance. In the case of deciduous trees this is achieved quite simply by shedding all the leaves in autumn. Evergreen trees have very much lower rates of transpiration than deciduous trees, reducing water loss by having needle-like leaves of small surface area (e.g. pines) and/or leaves with a thick waxy cuticle (e.g. Holly).

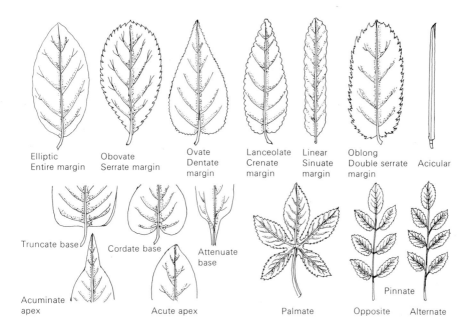

Elliptic
Entire margin

Obovate
Serrate margin

Ovate
Dentate
margin

Lanceolate
Crenate
margin

Linear
Sinuate
margin

Oblong
Double serrate
margin

Acicular

Truncate base

Cordate base

Attenuate
base

Acuminate
apex

Acute apex

Palmate

Pinnate

Opposite

Alternate

Leaves vary considerably in shape, texture, colour, size and arrangement from species to species and are perhaps the most valuable and easiest identification feature. When attempting to identify a species of tree, the leaves should be examined carefully and points such as the appearance of the leaf margin, general shape, presence of hairs and length of petiole noted. Differences in colour and texture between the top surface and underside can be important. For deciduous trees the autumn coloration is also a guide to identification. As the winter approaches the green chlorophyll in the leaves begins to break down and the red and yellow carotenoid pigments tend to predominate, changing the colour of the leaves to a range of reds, yellows and oranges. These autumn tints are characteristic of each species.

Yet another identification guide is the overall shape of a tree: the length of trunk and the way in which the branches spread. However, it must be remembered that the shape is not invariable; it is influenced by many factors such as the soil type, prevailing wind, surrounding vegetation and man's activity. For example, trees growing together in a wood, either planted or natural, are said to be close grown and will have a quite different shape from those of the same species growing away from other trees (open grown). A close grown tree will tend to be tall with a long trunk supporting a narrow crown as a result of competition for light, whereas an open grown tree will be shorter with a broad, low crown on a short, thick trunk.

For thousands of years man has made use of trees; cutting them down to provide timber for buildings or for fuel, trusting to nature to replace them and giving little thought to the time factors involved or the effect on the environment as a whole. A large tree may take hundreds of years to grow to its full height, providing food and shelter to generations of flora and fauna, and yet it can be felled in a matter of minutes. Only in relatively recent years has it at last become apparent that the Earth's stock of trees is diminishing at an alarming rate.

Over the past three hundred years in Britain a few private land-owners have made an effort to treat timber as a crop and have actively encouraged the introduction of some suitable species from abroad. However, this attitude has been the exception rather than the rule and by 1918, 90% of the commercial timber used in Britain was imported. Shortly after the First World War, the British Government instituted the Forestry Commission in an attempt to rectify this situation and encourage the use of land for forestry. The Commission has planted large areas of country with trees and has carried out much needed research. In recent years it has even opened its forests, where suitable, to the general public, providing a useful recreation facility with picnic sites and nature trails.

In urban areas too, trees are coming into their own and Local Authorities and Private Developers are now keen to allocate space for trees in new developments, along streets and in town parks. Trees particularly suitable for urban areas are those species and varieties that are known to be tolerant of air pollution, are relatively small and are resistant to aphid attack.

Insects

Most species of tree harbour a multitude of insects which may feed on the leaves, live under the bark or burrow in the timber. Although rarely occurring in sufficient numbers to seriously affect the health of the tree, most insects cause some damage or disfigurement by defoliation or sap sucking. More importantly they frequently act as transmitters of disease, spreading viruses and fungal spores from tree to tree. The most obvious example of this is the spread in recent years of Dutch elm disease which has decimated the elms once so common in the hedge-rows of southern and central England. This devastating fungal disease is transmitted largely by a small bark beetle which lays its eggs in the timber of elm.

It should, however, be pointed out that not all insects are harmful: many trees rely on insects for pollination and some insects parasitize or prey on detrimental species.

In this book we have listed a few of the insect species which may be found in association with certain trees. These lists are by no means intended to be comprehensive but should give an idea of the more common species which may be found.

Fungi

Because fungi have no chlorophyll and so cannot photosynthesise, they must obtain their nourishment from other sources. They are therefore either saprophytic, feeding on decaying organic matter, or parasitic, feeding on the living cells of other organisms.

Both saprophytic and parasitic fungi are commonly found in association with trees, either living on the tree itself or on the dead organic matter surrounding it.

Although some fungi are harmful, causing disease, generally weakening the tree or decaying constructional timber, many are beneficial or even essential for healthy growth. In larch forests, between spring and autumn, the fruiting bodies of the Larch Boletus (*Boletus elegans* Fries) are often seen under the larches, following lines radiating from the tree trunks. These fungi are in close association with the roots of the larch forming a symbiotic relationship of mutual benefit to both plants. This is known as a mycorrhyzal association.

Fungi also play an indispensable role along with bacteria in the woodland ecosystem, aiding the breakdown of plant and animal debris.

In this book we have listed a few of the macro-fungi likely to be found on or under each species of tree described. Many of these are not specific to particular trees and all produce fruit bodies visible to the naked eye.

A Note on Classification

Seed-bearing plants are divided into two major classes: the gymnosperms (Gymnospermae) in which the seeds are naked, and the angiosperms (Angiospermae) in which the seeds are enclosed within an ovary which later develops into a fruit. Trees occur in both classes. The conifers or softwoods are gymnosperms and produce unisexual flowers which have no petals or sepals and are entirely anemophilous (wind-pollinated). Most produce woody cones (e.g. Scots Pine) although in some species (e.g. Yew) the cone-scales become fleshy, forming a berry-like fruit.

The broad-leaved trees or hardwoods belong to a group of angiosperms called the dicotyledons, and have a great diversity of flower form and structure, some adapted to attract insect pollinators and some adapted for wind pollination.

Within this main grouping, trees are divided amongst a number of families (e.g. Fagaceae) each of which contains one or several genera (e.g. *Quercus*) sub-divided into species (e.g. *Quercus robur*). In this book the trees are arranged according to their families.

Salicaceae
Crack Willow—*Salix fragilis* L.

Crack Willow

Description
The Crack Willow is a rapid-growing, deciduous tree, which is very sturdy in appearance though unpredictable in shape and usually leaning when mature. It may reach a height of 27 m with a girth of up to 6 m. The trunk is stout, with obliquely wide-spreading branches which break easily. Tall crack willows are often stag-headed, but many are pollarded and so never attain much height. The average life-span is probably 200 years, but some specimens are said to be 1000 years old.

Timber
Sapwood white, heartwood pinkish, soft, tough, straight grained, finely textured, very light when seasoned, splits easily and not durable. Used for cart bottoms, barrows, children's toys, clog soles and artificial limbs. Makes excellent charcoal for medicinal purposes. Useless as fuel. S. 'Caerulea', a closely related tree, is used to make cricket bats.

Range and Habitat
Native range extends from W. Siberia to Iran, and covers Europe including England, Scotland and Wales. Doubtfully native to Ireland where, nevertheless, it is often planted. Prefers wet lowland habitats by streams and rivers, but not conservative in this respect. Broken twigs will strike readily almost anywhere.

Related Trees
The White Willow, S. *alba* L., is, in many aspects, similar to Crack Willow, but has a neater, narrower habit; silvery-grey foliage; smaller, finely dentate leaves 5–8 cm long, which are white silky pubescent above and below; and petioles without glands at apex. The twigs are supple and do not readily crack off at their base when pulled back. Native to Europe (including Britain), N. Africa and parts of Asia. Habitats similar to those of Crack Willow, and

White Willow

often pollarded. There is a weeping form 'Tristis'.

Associated Macro-fungi on Willows and Sallows
Terrestrial—*Tricholoma cingulatum* Fries; *Hebeloma leucosarx* P. D. Orton; *H. mesophaeum* (Pers.) Quél.; *H. testaceum* (Fries) Quél.; *Lactarius lacunarum* Hora. **Lignicolous**—*Daedalepsis rubescens* (Fries) Schroet.; *Pluteus salicinus* (Fries) Kumm.; *Phellinus igniarius* (Fries) Quél.; *Trametes suaveolens* (Fries) Fries.

Associated Insects on Willows and Sallows
Lepidoptera—Butterflies: *Apatura iris* L., Purple Emperor, larvae feed openly on leaves. Macro-moths: *Smerinthus ocellata* L., Eyed Hawk; *Leucoma salicis* L., White Satin; *Agrochola litura* L., Brown Spot Pinion; *Orthosia gracilis* Denis & Schiff., Powdered Quaker; *Epione repandaria* Hufn., Bordered Beauty; *Earias clorana* L., Cream-bordered Green Pea; *Xanthia togata* Esper, Pink-barred Sallow, larvae feed on catkins when young, low plants later. *Hydriomena furcata* Thunb., July Highflyer, larvae feed on leaves. *Cossus cossus* L., Goat Moth, larvae feed in timber (also in poplar, ash and oak). *Sphecia bembeciformis* Hübn., Lunar Hornet Clearwing, larvae feed in timber (also poplar). (Continued on p. 18.)

General Information
Bark contains the drug salicine. Willow is the emblem of grief, hence the term 'To wear the willow'. The rootlets of White Willow, seen under water, are whitish in colour; those of Crack Willow are red. The family as a whole pose a difficult subject, there being so many subspecies and hybrids, identification is often problematical. Crack Willow is definitely not a tree for the average garden: its branching, brittle roots will block drains and disturb house foundations. It should

not be planted by small, still ponds as the dropping leaves will poison the water. Wildlife value good.

Bark: Dull grey and smooth when young, becoming scaly; mature trees dark grey, rough and with a network of fairly shallow ridges.

Twigs: Characteristic in that when pulled sharply back they easily break off at the base with an audible crack. Olive brown, smooth and shiny, tough and flexible, frequently interlaced and crossing each other. Buds smooth, long, pointed and adpressed to the twigs with a single visible bud-scale; may be yellow, pale green, reddish to nearly black.

Leaves: Unfold April. Alternate, simple and elliptic-lanceolate, 7–15 cm long. Light green and slightly pubescent at first; soon glossy green above, greyish-green beneath, and entirely glabrous. Stipules long-cordate. Autumn tints yellow to brown.

Flowers: April. Dioecious, entomophilous. Male catkins 2.5–5 cm long, semi-erect, shortly stalked, fairly stout and yellow in bloom. Female catkins 3–5 cm long when in bloom, developing into fruiting catkins 10 cm long in May. They are semi-erect, slender and purplish-green; when ripe show white fluff.

Fruit: Ripen May–June, in the catkins, each a slender, stalked capsule tapering at the apex and covered in white down which assists dispersal on the wind.

A Bark, Crack Willow.
B Catkins ♀, Crack Willow.
C Leaves and seed capsules, Crack Willow.

Salicaceae
Great Sallow or Goat Willow—*Salix caprea* L.

Great Sallow

Common
Sallow

Description

The Sallow is a rapid-growing, deciduous, bushy shrub or small tree which rarely grows over 6 m high. When allowed to reach such heights, it becomes top-heavy and often leans or even falls over. The trunk is short, dividing into several ascending branches. It is not long living as a tree, but when coppiced periodically it will regenerate indefinitely.

Timber

Tough and elastic, unsubstantial and of no commercial value. Sometimes used for making clothes pegs.

Range and Habitat

Native to Europe including Britain, also N.E. Africa. A pioneer coloniser found almost anywhere on any substrate, wet or well drained.

Related Trees

The Common or Grey Sallow, *S. cinerea* L., is similar to Great Sallow, very variable, often hybridising, and with similar range and habitat. Leaves usually narrower and shorter than Great Sallow, tip not turned downwards, pubescence thin on underside and often rust coloured; young shoots long remaining pubescent. Bark stripped from substantial twigs reveals ridged wood beneath; this is smooth in Great Sallow. Weeping forms of both species are very attractive but require cutting back yearly.

Associated Macro-fungi

See under Crack Willow.

Associated Insects on Willows and Sallows

Continued from p. 16. *Pelosia muscerda* Hufn., Dotted Footman, larvae in lichens on bark. *Scoliopteryx libatrix* L., Herald; *Catocala nupta* L., Red Underwing; *Pheosia tremula* Clerck, Swallow Prominent; *Harpyia furcula* Clerck, Sallow Kitten; *Orthosia advena* Denis & Schiff., Northern Drab; *Dasychira fascelina* L., Dark Tussock, larvae feed on leaves. **Micro-lepidoptera** —*Acleris emargana* F., larvae in folded leaf. *Epinotia cruciana* L.; *Pammene populana* F., in spun shoots. *Epinotia subocellana* Donov.; *Teleiodes notatella* Hübn., larvae feed on leaves. *Apotomis capreana* Hübn., larvae in spun shoots. *Agonopteryx ocellana* F., larvae in spun or rolled leaves. *Argyresthia pygmaëlla* Hübn., larvae in shoots or catkins. *Yponomeuta rorrella* Hübn., larvae gregarious, in web on leaves. *Coleophora albidella* Herr.-Schaeff., in erect black pistol-shaped case on upperside of leaves. *Glyphipteryx Iathamella* Fletch., in bark. *Phyllocnistis saligna* Zell., in galleries of bark when young, later in leaves. *Ectoedemia intimella* Zell., in blotch mine. *Phyllonorycter salicicolella* Sircom; *Nepticula vimineticola* Frey; *N. salicis* Staint.; *Lithocolletis viminetorum* Staint.; *L. viminiella* Staint., leaf miners. **Coleoptera**—Leaf beetles: *Lochmaea capreae* L.; *Luperus longicornis* F.; *Galerucella lineola* F.; *Phyllodecta vitellinae* L. Weevils: *Cryptorhynchus lapathi* L. Longhorn beetles: *Aromia moschata* L., larvae in wood. **Homoptera** —Aphids: *Chaitophorus beuthani* Boern.; *C. vitellinae* Schrank; *C. niger* Mordv.; *C. truncatus* Hausm.; *C. capreae* Mosely. Scale insects: *Chionaspis salicis* L., forms scales on bark (causes willow scale). Froghoppers: *Aphrophora salicina* Goeze. Leaf-hoppers: *Idiocerus rutilans* Kirschb.; *I. stigmaticalis* Lewis; *Macropsis infuscata* Sahlb. **Hymenoptera** —Sawflies: *Pamphilius gyllenhali* Dahl., larvae live in rolled leaf margins. *Xiphydria prolongata* Geoff., larvae in wood (also on poplar and elm on Continent). *Trichiosoma vitellinae* L.; *T. lucorum* L., free feeding on leaves (*lucorum* also on birch). *Amauronematus miltonotus* Zadd., larvae on leaves. *A. viduatus* Zett., larvae on leaves. *A. fasciatus* Konow, larvae on leaves. *Euura atra* Jur., larvae solitary in stems. *E. amerinae* L., larvae massed together in irregular walnut-like gall on twigs (also poplar). (Continued on p. 20.)

General Information
When in bloom referred to as 'palm' and used in decoration of churches and homes at Eastertide. The bloom attracts innumerable, night- and day-flying insects. The seed down is often used by Goldfinches, Redpolls and Common Linnets for lining their nests. Sallow is generally good for wildlife. The tree is commonly called Saugh, especially in northern Britain.

Bark: Pale or greenish-grey and smooth when young; later smooth with shallow fissures.

Twigs: Stout, olive grey at first and pubescent; very soon glabrous, brown and shiny. Buds ovoid, pointed and reddish-brown.

Leaves: Unfold April. Alternate, variable, broadly ovate or elliptical, 5–10 cm long, margin crenate or entire; broad for a member of this family. Thick and woolly to the touch, wrinkled, with tip turned downwards. Dull green above, greyish-green and woolly beneath with prominent venation. Petiole about 1 cm long and pubescent; stipules caducous.

Flowers: Before leaves, March or April. Dioecious, entomophilous. Male catkin buds noticeably silvery long before they finally open ('pussy willows'). When in full bloom they are golden yellow, 2.5–4 cm long, oblong-cylindrical, soon fading to creamy-yellow. Female buds similar to males, lengthening into greyish-green, spiky-looking catkins.

Fruit: Ripen and shed May. Dispersal wind assisted. A downy white capsule about 6 mm long, with tapering beak.

A Catkins ♂ (left) and ♀ (right), Great Sallow.
B Leaves, Great Sallow.
C Ripe seed capsules, Great Sallow.

Salicaceae
Common Osier—*Salix viminalis* L.

Common Osier

Description
The Common Osier is a rapid-growing, small, deciduous tree up to 9 m high, bearing long, straight, twiggy branches. However, it is rarely seen as a tree, more often being coppiced to produce a small, round shrub with dense foliage. In some areas it is cultivated and cut yearly.

Timber
Tough and elastic, unsubstantial and of no commercial value. Coppiced shoots used in the making of baskets, lobster pots, fish traps, bird cages, hurdles etc.

Range and Habitat
Native to western and central Europe including Britain, less common than formerly, due mainly to the decline in the basket-making industry. Grows almost anywhere, but prefers damp lowland soils.

Related Trees
The Almond-leaved Willow, *S. triandra* L., differs from Common Osier in its oblong-lanceolate, serrated, glabrous leaves, which appear with the flowers; each male flower with three stamens. The bark is flaky, peeling off to reveal orange underbark. The Purple Osier, *S. purpurea* L., in tree form is usually smaller than either Almond-leaved Willow or Common Osier, with smooth grey, non-fissured bark; shiny and purplish twigs; sub-opposite leaves, variable in shape, finely serrate and glaucous, turn black in autumn before being shed. Flowers appear before leaves, each male flower purple-red with 2 stamens united into an entire filament. Much favoured as an osier and there are many hybrid permutations. The Creeping Willow, *S. repens* L., could hardly be described as a tree, being so small that it may be passed unnoticed. It has tough wandering stems which are mainly procumbent, creeping under the ground and amongst other vegetation, rooting here and there at the base.

Common and native in dune-slacks, moist peaty heaths and commons.

Associated Macro-fungi
See under Crack Willow.

Associated Insects on Willows and Sallows
Continued from p. 19. *Pontania piliserra* Thomson; *P. anglica* Cameron, larvae in rolled leaf margins. *P. puella* Thomson, larvae in rolled leaf margins. *P. proxima* Lepel., in bean-shaped gall on leaves. *P. pedunculi* Hart., hairy pea-like gall on leaves. *Nematus melanocephalus* Hart., and other species of the genus. **Diptera**—Gall midges: *Iteomyia capreae* Winn., forms green pouches along lateral veins of leaves. *Rhabdophaga heterobia* Loew, forms catkin gall in spring, later forms rosette galls in leaf buds. *R. rosaria* Loew, causes terminal leaves to be shortened and clustered.

General Information
James Brown, in his mid-19th-century book *The Forester*, gives an interesting account on the management of osier beds. He states that before planting, the ground should be trenched, dunged and cleaned. After planting, the whips should remain uncut for two years in order to strengthen the stocks, but should be cut over at the end of the second year, preferably in February. In other words one year's growth is used by the basket maker. If the crop is intended for coopers' hoops, growth of two or even three years will be required. In cutting them over for the first time, three buds should be left from the bottom and the cut made in a sloping direction, but with later cuttings the shoots should be taken away, leaving only the swollen parts from which they grew. At the time of Brown's writing the basket-making industry, which previously had enjoyed great importance in Britain, was beginning to decline. Sadly, today it has declined still further. Various local names are used

to distinguish between osier rods of different quality within a species. For instance rods of the Almond-leaved Willow are known as black mauls, green sucklings, black hollander or glibskins depending on their state of growth.

Bark: Greyish-brown and smooth at first; later lightly and vertically fissured revealing orange underbark.

Twigs: Straight, flexible and green, tomentose when young; later glabrous, olive or brown. Buds small, narrow and yellowish.

Leaves: Unfold April. Alternate, linear-lanceolate, margin entire or obscurely serrate, wavy, often curled under, 10–25 cm long, 1–3 cm broad. Glabrous and dark green above, with prominent venation, silky shiny grey pubescence beneath. Petiole short; stipules lanceolate. Autumn tint yellow.

Flowers: Early April, before leaves. Dioecious, entomophilous. Male catkins 2–2.5 cm long, in terminal clusters, cylindrical, yellow in bloom, each flower with 2 stamens; scales obovate, densely pubescent, yellowish-green to brown, with blackish tips. Female catkins 8–12 mm broad, greenish, stigma yellow.

Fruit: Ripen and shed June. Dispersal wind assisted. A tapering downy capsule with broad base.

A Catkins ♂ (left) and ♀ (right), Common Osier.
B Leaves and seed capsules, Common Osier.
C Seed capsules, Creeping Willow.

Salicaceae
White Poplar—*Populus alba* L.

Description
The White Poplar is a vigorous, freely suckering, deciduous tree, up to 18–24 m high. It is slender in habit, broadest at the summit and often leaning, with light, twisting, spreading branches which ascend steeply, level out and finally droop slightly. It has a life-span of about 100 years.

Timber
White, soft and light, fire resistant, easily split, difficult to saw. General uses include flooring, match-boxes, chip-boxes, plywood and pulp.

Range and Habitat
Native to western and central Europe, also central Asia. Possibly indigenous to parts of Britain, but now often planted and naturalised, most commonly in coastal sandy areas where it thrives well. Tolerant of air pollution and sea-laden winds. Prefers moist open soils in open lowland areas with adequate sunlight.

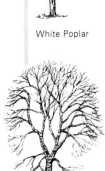

White Poplar

Related Trees
The Grey Poplar, *P. canescens* (Aiton) Sm., is similar to White Poplar with characteristics intermediate between it and the Aspen, *P. tremula*, but is more vigorous and bigger than either tree. Native in much of temperate Europe, and thought to be so in parts of Midland and southern England. The leaves are broadly ovate, broadest below the middle, with 4–5 blunt, broad teeth on each side; grey pubescent on both sides at first, soon glossy and glabrous above. The petiole is barely flattened or not at all; catkin scales are deeply cut. The bark of adult Grey Poplar is more rugged than that of White Poplar.

Associated Macro-fungi
Terrestrial—*Tricholoma populinum* J. Lange; *Lactarius controversus* (Fries) Fries; *Boletus aurantiacum* (Fries) S. F. Gray; *Boletus duriusculus* (Schulz.) Sing.; *Mitromorpha hybrida* (Fries)

Grey Poplar

Léville. **Lignicolous**—*Agrocybe cylindracea* (Fries) Maire; *Pholiota destruens* (Brond.) Gill.; *Bjerkandera fumosa* (Fries) Karst.; *Oxyporus populinus* (Fries) Donk.

Associated Insects
Lepidoptera—Moths: *Gypsonoma aceriana* Dupon., larvae in shoots, leaves and stems etc. *Acleris rufana* Denis & Schiff., larvae in spun leaves (also on *Myrica* and *Salix*). *Gelechia nigra* Haworth, larvae between two leaves spun together (also on Aspen). **Homoptera**—Aphids: *Chaitophorus albus* Mordv.; *C. populeti* Panz. Leaf-hoppers: *Idiocerus distinguendus* Kirschb. Possibly a number of insects recorded from Black Poplar will also occur on White and Grey Poplar.

General Information
Pliny stated that the White Poplar always turned its leaves to an opposite quarter of the heavens immediately the summer solstice was passed. In mythology the tree was consecrated to Hercules. John Evelyn recommended it in the 17th century as a fit tree to plant for quick landscaping round newly built country houses. Because of its vigorous, spreading root system, it is not recommended for planting in small gardens, on golf courses, or near buildings.

Bark: Very smooth for many years, greenish-white to grey and covered with copious dark, diamond-shaped lenticels arranged in horizontal lines. Eventually becomes black, rough and furrowed on the lower part of the main stem.

Twigs: Young shoots green, white-tomentose; older twigs brown, uneven, knobbly and glabrous. Buds ovoid, orange-brown, and white-tomentose.

Leaves: Unfold April–May. Alternate, variable in size and shape, 2.5–10 cm long, roundish-cordate, and shallowly sinuately lobed, more acutely 5-lobed

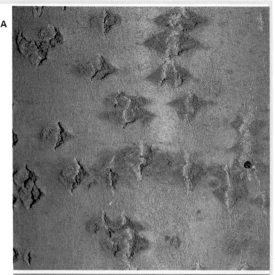

on young vigorous shoots; outline
broadly reminiscent of juvenile Ivy
leaf. Unfold completely white-tomentose,
soon becoming dark green and glabrous
above; greyish-white tomentose beneath.
Petiole long, tomentose beneath.
Autumn tints brown, sometimes red.

Flowers: April, before leaves. Dioecious
(males predominate), anemophilous.
Male catkins 5–10 cm long, pendant,
crimson and grey, hairy with dentate
scales, soon shed. Female catkins
shorter, 5 cm long, greenish-yellow.

Fruit: Ripen June. A small, recurved
capsule; seeds black and oval with long
silky hairs. Very few germinate.

A Bark, White Poplar.
B Catkins ♂ (above) and ♀ (below), White
Poplar.
C Leaves, White Poplar.

Salicaceae
Aspen—*Populus tremula* L.

Aspen

Description
When full grown, the Aspen is an erect, elegant and delicate tree with short slender branches which droop at their extremities. It is characterised in spring and summer by its trembling, rustling foliage, a feature shared by other poplars, but not to the same extent. In ideal conditions it will reach a height of 24 m and be mature at about 50 years. The Aspen produces suckers freely, and these are eagerly browsed by cattle and deer; in consequence the trees are often seen as misshapen bushes in scrub-like stands.

Timber
Green timber heavy, but swiftly dries out to become very light, both in weight and colour. Easily split and does not splinter. Many commercial uses, for example, matches, match- and chip-boxes, surgical splints, wagon bottoms, floor boards, clogs and pulp. Virtually useless as fuel.

Range and Habitat
Indigenous to the Arctic and N. Temperate Zones of Europe, N. Africa and northern Asia. Widespread and native throughout Britain. Prefers a soil high in organic matter and moisture retaining, especially in river valleys, but will subsist on gravels if not deprived of water. Found growing naturally up to heights of 1200 m in the Bavarian Alps.

Related Trees
The American Aspen, *P. tremuloides* Michx., native to N. America, is similar to *P. tremula* but usually smaller in stature with smaller leaves.

Associated Macro-fungi
Terrestrial—*Tricholoma populinum* J. Lange; *Boletus duriusculus* (Schulz.) Sing. **Lignicolous**—*Oxyporus populinus* (Fries) Donk; *Bjerkandera fumosa* (Fries) Karst; *Agrocybe cylindracea* (Fries) Maire.

Associated Insects
Lepidoptera—Moths: *Nephopteryx hostilis* Steph.; *Gypsonoma nitidulana* Lienig & Zell.; *Epinotia cinereana* Haworth; *E. maculana* F., larvae spin leaves together. *Nepticula assimilella* Zell.; *Ectoedemia argyropeza* Zell., larvae are leaf miners. **Coleoptera**—Beetles: *Chrysomela tremula* F.; *Zeugophora subspinosa* F., leaf feeders. Weevils: *Byctiscus populi* L.; *Dorytomus tortrix* L.; *D. affinis* Payk. **Homoptera**—Aphids: *Chaitophorus tremulae* Koch. **Hymenoptera**—Sawflies: *Euura amerinae* L.; *Pteronidea fuscomaculata* Foerst., larvae feed on leaves. *Heterarthrus ochropoda* Klug., larvae are leaf miners. **Diptera**—*Syndiplosis petioli* Kief., larvae in gall on leaf petiole. *Harmandia globuli* Rübs., larvae in small brown gall near leaf midrib.

General Information
Legend has it that Christ's cross was made of aspenwood. Not a tree for the small garden and should never be planted near buildings or drains.

Bark: Pale greenish-grey, smooth and thin when young, with horizontal lenticels; the bole becoming darker and fissured with age, often with burrs.

Twigs: Irregularly wavy, olive grey tending to brownish at the extremities. Winter buds scaly, pointed, date-coloured and shiny.

Leaves: Unfold April–May. On mature trees almost circular in outline, 4 cm in diameter and broadly dentate. Slightly pubescent at first but soon glabrous both sides. The leaves of suckers are cordate and up to 10 cm broad, with entire margins. Petiole long, flattened and set at right-angles to the leaves; hence the tremulous habit. Autumn tint vivid yellow.

Flowers: March. Dioecious, anemophilous. Male catkins 5–8 cm long, silky and purplish-grey at first, then showy in red and yellow, finally brown. Female catkins silky and greenish with reddish brown bracts and grey hairs.

Fruit: Ripen May. Tiny black seeds contained in egg-shaped woody capsules, each of which carries a cottony appendage. Dispersed by wind. Only a small proportion arrive on a suitably damp substrate and germinate quickly, the majority lose their vigour and perish.

A Bark, Aspen. **B** Catkins ♂ Aspen.
C Leaves, Aspen.

Salicaceae
Black Poplar—*Populus nigra* var. *betulifolia* (Pursh) Torr.

Black Poplar

Lombardy Poplar

Description
This vigorous, deciduous tree is so often pollarded or mutilated, it is rarely allowed to show its true stature in Britain. When full grown the Black Poplar is a massive, dark-looking tree, nearly always leaning away from the prevailing wind. The rather sparse, ascending, heavy branches break out from the trunk fairly low down, spread widely and then arch downwards. It is a very hardy tree, up to 30 m high. Invariably the trunk and larger branches carry large, dark burrs.

Timber
White or pale brown, woolly, soft, tough, straight grained and not at all durable; often spoiled by insect larvae.

Range and Habitat
Native to northern and western Europe. The variety *betulifolia* differs from the type, which is native to Europe and western Asia, in its downy petioles, main veins and flower stalks. It is the variety most often seen in Britain and, because of its resistance to air pollution, it is commonly planted in urban areas of N.W. England where it is known as the 'Manchester Poplar'. It will thrive almost anywhere.

Related Trees
The Lombardy Poplar, *Populus nigra* 'Italica', needs little description. A male clone, propagated from a cutting, was introduced to Britain from Lombardy in 1758. The tree grows to 30 m in height and has a straight, fluted trunk bearing steeply ascending branches. It is very narrow in habit, often broadest midway up the tree and the petioles and shoots are glabrous. There are many hybrid poplars grown in Britain and Europe derived from crosses between *P. nigra* and the N. American species *P. deltoides*. These make useful amenity or timber trees.

Associated Macro-fungi
As for White Poplar.

Associated Insects
Lepidoptera—Moths: *Laothoe populi* L., Poplar Hawk; *Eligmodonta ziczac* L., Pebble Prominent; *Cerura vinula* L., Puss Moth (also on sallow and willow); *Harpyia bifida* Brahm, Poplar Kitten; *Tethea* or Denis & Schiff., Poplar Lutestring; *Acronicta megacephala* Denis & Schiff., Poplar Grey; larvae on leaves. *Gypsonoma aceriana* Dupon., larvae in shoots, leaves and stems etc. *G. minutana* Hübn., larvae between two leaves spun together. *Gelechia muscosella* Zell., larvae in catkins (also on sallow and willow). *Phyllocnistis unipunctella* Steph., leaf miner. **Coleoptera**—Leaf beetles: *Chrysomela populi* L., Longhorn beetles: *Saperda populnea* L., in swollen stems (also on birch). Weevils: *Dorytomus validirostris* Gyll.; *Cryptorhynchus lapathi* L., larvae in wood, adults on leaves. **Homoptera**—Leaf-hoppers: *Idiocerus vitreus* F. (sometimes on sallow); *I. fulgidus* F. (also on Lombardy Poplar). Aphids: *Chaitophorus leucomelas* Koch (also on Lombardy Poplar); *Pemphigus bursarius* L., leaf petioles distorted. *P. spirothecae* Pass., leaf petiole distorted into a spiral. Scale insects: *Chionaspis salicis* L., causes poplar and willow scale. **Hymenoptera**—Sawflies: *Messa hortulana* Klug, leaf miner. *Trichiocampus viminalis* L., larvae free-living, but gregarious on leaves (sometimes on sallow and willow).

General Information
Black poplars should never be planted near houses, on golf courses, by bowling greens, or around fields on heavy land; their water demands may well cause shrinkage and searching rootlets will completely block field drains.

Bark: Adult trees dark ash grey to very

dark brown, rough, deeply fissured with broad ridges, straight or sinuously patterned.

Twigs: Cylindrical, slender, pale yellow at first, later grey; young shoots pubescent. Buds viscid, narrowly conical, pointed and rich brown.

Leaves: Unfold late April–May. Alternate, triangular to ovate, 5–10 cm long, with fine, bluntly serrate, narrowly translucent margin. Unfold with a brownish cast, soon bright, shiny green with pubescent main veins. Petiole 4 cm long, slender, compressed and pubescent. Autumn tint yellow.

Flowers: March. Dioecious, anemophilous. Male catkins pendulous, lax, showy crimson in full bloom, 5 cm long. Female catkins greenish-white.

Fruit: Ripen May–June. A brownish woody capsule which splits open, shedding ripe, cottony seeds which are rarely fertile.

A Bark, Black Poplar.
B Catkins ♂ Black Poplar.
C Catkins ♀ Black Poplar.
D Fruit and leaves, Black Poplar.

Juglandaceae
Common Walnut—*Juglans regia* L.

Walnut

Description
The Common Walnut is an attractive, long-lived, rapid-growing, deciduous tree which usually grows up to 12–18 m high, but may reach a height of 30 m. The trunk is bulky in proportion to the height and the lower branches are substantial and tortuous, ascending to form a large spreading head. In winter the tree has a gnarled and rugged appearance, but in summer this feature is lost in a handsome foliage of warm green.

Timber
White in young trees, brown in mature specimens; coarse grained, tough, strong, durable and beautifully marked, taking a high polish. In great demand for cabinet-work, furniture veneers and gun stocks.

Range and Habitat
Native to the Balkans, from the Himalayas to the Far East and introduced to many other parts of the world. The date of introduction to Britain is obscure and although the 15th century is often quoted, it would seem reasonable to suppose that the Romans brought it here. Today fairly common in southern counties, but infrequent north of the Midlands; thriving only on well-drained, light, base-rich soils and in good light.

Related Trees
Including the hickories (*Carya* spp.) and wingnuts (*Pterocarya* spp.) there are about 50 species in the walnut family. All are monoecious with substantial, alternate, exstipulate, compound-pinnate leaves. The Black Walnut, *J. nigra* L., a native of eastern N. America but introduced into Europe, has dark brown to black bark, with fissures, and large pinnate leaves with 11–23 leaflets.

Associated Macro-fungi
None specific in Britain.

Associated Fauna
Acarine gall mite *Eriophyes tristriatus typicus* Nal, on leaves.

General Information
The Walnut has no affinity to a wall; the name is derived from the word 'wälsh' or 'welsh' which means foreign. The nut kernel contains an edible oil which is also suitable for burning or making paint. All parts of the tree produce juices which are good brown dyeing agents. The young unripe drupes are often pickled for culinary purposes. The Walnut is a decorative tree but unsuitable for the small garden. Saplings have thick, deeply penetrating roots and care should be taken not to break these if transplanting is necessary.

Bark: Pale grey and smooth when young; later, still retaining its light colour, the surface is scored into deep, longitudinal, irregular, flat-faced ridges.

Twigs: Dark green to dark brown, coarse, glabrous and shining. Although they give a visual impression of strength and solidity, when handled they are easily broken, as the core is merely a spongy pith which is discontinuous with parallel cross-partitions. Winter buds bold, stumpy and almost black, set spirally on twigs.

Leaves: Unfold May–June. Alternate, compound-pinnate and exstipulate, usually with 7 or 9 leaflets, up to 20 cm long, 10 cm broad, elliptic, sub-sessile and obscurely serrate. The terminal leaflet is the largest. At first orange-brown and under a lens appear as if powdered with gold, soon becoming dark yellowish-green with yellow veins. The crushed foliage has a distinct aromatic scent. Autumn tint brown.

Flowers: May–June, before leaves. Monoecious, anemophilous. Male catkins borne on shoots of previous year, 5–15 cm long, drooping, greenish and impressive; calyx of 2–5 green

scales, stamens numerous and blackish. Female flowers solitary or in clusters, terminal on shoots of the year; green, small and erect, shaped like Italian amphorae, each bearing 2 or 3 recurved stigmas.

Fruit: Ripen late September–October. The ovary of the fertile flower expands into a smooth, green, sub-globose, 2-valved drupe up to 5 cm long. Eventually the outer green flesh sloughs away, revealing the pale brown wrinkled nutshell with a large seam down the middle, within which is the brain-like lobed kernel with white flesh, covered in a thin brown skin. This fruit is held in high regard as food. In northern Britain the crop is uncertain and rarely ripens.

A Bark, Common Walnut.
B Flowers ♀ (left), catkins ♂ (right), Common Walnut.
C Leaves and fruit, Common Walnut.

Betulaceae
Silver Birch—*Betula pendula* Roth.

Silver Birch

Description
The Silver Birch is the most graceful and climatically hardy of British trees. It never attains a great size and although it can reach a height of 30 m, it usually averages 12–18 m, with a girth of 30–38 cm. Short-lived, with a life-span rarely exceeding 80 years, it often succumbs to attacks by parasitic fungi very early in life. Normally the tree is single-stemmed, with a straight, tapering trunk bearing many light, shortish and steeply ascending branches which are often pendulous. It is a rapid-growing species, mature at about 40 years old, but only develops into a small bush towards the northern limits of its range.

Timber
Pale yellow, moderately hard and strong but without lasting qualities, especially outdoors. Used for veneers, plywood, cheap furniture etc. Burns well. The bark is waterproof and used for roofing and tanning; the twigs for brooms.

Range and Habitat
Native to Europe and Asia Minor, but represented by many allied species in N. America, India, China and Japan. Birches will thrive almost anywhere and are great colonisers, especially on heath or peaty lands. They are light loving.

Related Trees
The Hairy Birch, *B. pubescens* Ehrh., of Europe (including Britain) has hairy twigs and petioles; the leaves are rounded and short-pointed.
The Dwarf Birch, *B. nana* L., native to boggy and mountainous areas of northern and central Europe, Asia and N. America, is rarely more than a creeping bush with small, very shortly petiolate, rounded, crenate leaves.
The Canoe Birch or Paper-bark Birch, *B. papyrifera* Marsh., of northern N. America and introduced into Europe, has creamy-white bark on young trunks which peels in strips revealing pale orange colour beneath. This bark was used by N. American Indians in the construction of their canoes.

Associated Macro-fungi
Terrestrial—*Amanita muscaria* (Fries) Hook., Fly Agaric; *A. fulva* Secr., Tawny Grisette; *Boletus versipellis* Fries & Hök; *Lactarius turpis* (Weinm.) Fries, Base Toadstool; *L. victus* (Fries) Fries; *L. torminosus* (Fries) S. F. Gray; *Tricholoma fulvum* (Fries) Sacc.
Lignicolous—*Fomes fomentarius* (Fries) Kickx., Tinder Fungus; *Piptoporus betulinus* (Fries) Karst., Birch Bracket; *Lenzites betulina* Fries.

Associated Insects
Lepidoptera—Moths: *Pheosia gnoma* F., Lesser Swallow Prominent; *Achyla flavicornis* L., Yellow-horned; *Archiearis parthenias* L., Orange Underwing, larvae feed on leaves. *Phyllonorycter cavella* Zell.; *P. anderidae* Fletch.; *Stigmella betulicola* Staint.; *Nepticula continuella* Staint., larvae feed in leaf-mines. **Coleoptera**—Weevils: *Byctiscus betulae* L.; *Apion simile* Kirby.
Hymenoptera—Sawflies: *Croesus latipes* de Vill.; *Cimbex femorata* L.; *Nematinus acuminatus* Thomson.
Diptera—Gall midges: *Semudobia betulae* Winn., in fruits. *Masslongia rubra* Kief., in swollen midrib. *Plemeliella betulicola* Kief., in young terminal leaves. All apparently restricted to birch; there are very many other polyphagous species.

General Information
A strong wine fermented from the sap of birch trees used to be highly recommended for medicinal purposes. The witches' broom seen on these trees is usually caused by a micro-fungus which alters the structure of the cell tissues. Birches are desirable trees for the garden; they are ornamental, take up little space and, because they proffer little shade, a wealth of ground flora can develop beneath them.

Bark: Thin, smooth and purplish-brown in very young trees and on light branches of older trees. The bark on the trunk and heavier branches of all trees becomes scaly, silvery-white or reddish-white, with darker transverse lenticels and rough black markings; the base often roughly fissured and blackish with age.

Twigs: Dark purplish-brown with rough greyish-white warts, supple and thin, pendulous or not. Buds alternate, ovoid and dark scaled.

Leaves: Unfold April–May. May be rounded-triangular or diamond-shape in outline, but always with a long-pointed apex and protruding narrow teeth, each separated by 2–4 smaller teeth. Light green, becoming darker and finally yellow in the fall. Petiole long and glabrous.

Flowers: Monoecious, anemophilous. Male catkins are pendant, usually in pairs at the end of shoots and are visible in autumn, lengthening to about 5 cm in April, purplish-brown at first, then yellow with pollen. Female catkins, borne on the same twigs as the males, are erect and small by comparison, green and prickly to the naked eye, having a green and purple triangular pattern under lens. Later they develop into pendant cone-like bodies, turning brown and ripening in autumn. Meanwhile the male catkins have dried and fallen in May.

Fruit: Produced at about 10 years old. Once mature, fruiting is regular and prolific. The minute nuts or seeds are delicately winged and freed from the cones by wind action.

A Bark, Silver Birch.
B Catkins ♀ (above) and ♂ (below), Silver Birch.
C Mature ♀ catkins (left), next year's ♂ catkins (right), Silver Birch.

Betulaceae
Common or Black Alder—*Alnus glutinosa* Gaertn.

Description
Normally, because of the Alder's readiness to throw suckers from the base, it only develops into a large, multi-stemmed bush. However, in a controlled environment, it will grow into a single-stemmed tree, up to 18 m high, with a narrow, pyramidal habit of many ascending, slender branches and sombre foliage. It has a life-span of up to 150 years, but, like the birch, it often succumbs to disease when quite young.

Timber
White, turns reddish when newly cut and dries out to pink; soft and light, splits readily when dry. Excellent for underwater use, e.g. piles, becoming very hard when immersed in water. Used in the past for making clog soles, water barrel staves, weatherboards and fine charcoal for gunpowder. The wood, being knotty and easily carved, is valuable to the turner and cabinet-maker.

Range and Habitat
Native to Europe, Asia Minor and N. Africa. Also found as an introduced species in N. America. Essentially a tree of damp places, especially stream and river banks, from their source almost to the sea; also lakesides and lowland swamps. Useful in that the roots are nitrogen fixing and bind the substrate, thereby checking erosion. Shallow but firm rooting and tolerant of pollution.

Related Trees
There are 30 known alder species from both the northern and southern hemispheres. The Grey Alder, *A. incana* (L.) Moench, is native to continental Europe and naturalised in parts of Britain. It has a smooth, grey bark with few fissures, and leaves with pointed tips which have a grey pubescence on underside when young. Italian Alder, *A. cordata* Desf., introduced into Britain, has a smooth, greyish bark, rather glossy cordate leaves with

abruptly pointed apices and noticeably larger cones than either Common or Grey Alder. An attractive tree becoming popular for parks and garden planting.

Associated Macro-fungi
Terrestrial—*Boletus lividus* (Bull.) Sacc.; *Naucoria escharoides* (Fries) Kumm.; *N. scolecina* (Fries) Quél.; *Lactarius obscuratus* (Lasch) Fries. **Lignicolous**—*Clavariadelphus fistulosis* var. *contorta* (Fries) Corner; *Exidia glandulosa* (St Amans) Fries; *Inonotus radiatus* (Fries) Karst.; *Plicaturiopsis crispa* (Fries) Reid.

Associated Insects
Lepidoptera—Moths: *Apatele alni* L., Alder Moth; *Harpyia bicuspis* Borkh., Alder Kitten; *Hydriomena coerulata* F., May Highflyer, larvae feed on leaves. *Phyllonorycter froelichiella* Zell., larvae in large leaf mine. *Stigmella alnetella* Staint., larvae in long slender mine on underside of leaf. **Coleoptera**—Leaf beetles: *Chrysomela aena* L.; *Agelastica alni* L. **Heteroptera**—Bugs: *Pterocallis alni* DeGeer. **Diptera**—True flies: *Dasyneura alni* Loew, larvae mine leaves causing galls.

General Information
In some parts of Britain the Alder is known by the name of Aller or Howler. Long ago the leaves were accredited with various virtues, they were brought into houses to rid them of fleas or used as poultices on burns and inflammations, also applied to refresh tired feet. As garden or roadside trees alders are useful but most have little appeal. Extensively planted in recent years on industrial waste heaps and motorway embankments.

Bark: Smooth and greyish or purplish-brown in semimature trees; greyish-brown to black, very rugged and fissured in older trees. Used in the manufacture of dyes.

Twigs: Slightly zig-zag and brittle,

Common Alder

greenish-brown to purplish-brown.
Buds shortly stalked, obtuse, green,
later purplish-brown.

Leaves: Unfold April. Alternate,
inversely cordate, 6.5–15 cm long, apex
truncate or notched, margin irregularly
serrate. Glutinous at first, tufts of
whitish down in vein angles on
underside. Petiole short; stipulate. The
tree retains its leaves until late in the
year; they turn brown before they fall.

Flowers: February–March. Monoecious,
anemophilous. Male catkins in groups
of up to 5 are present in the autumn,
pendant, cylindrical and 5–10 cm long;
reddish-yellow and consisting of many
flowers. Female catkins small, purplish-
brown, hard, scaled, bud-like, in semi-
erect clusters on stalks adjacent to
those bearing male catkins. In June the
fertilised female flowers will have
developed into green, closed, 'cedar-
cone-like' objects 1–2 cm long.

Fruit: Ripen October–December. A
woody, brown to black, open cone;
bearing, inside, 1-celled nutlets which
are without true wings, but with built-in
air-tight cavities enabling them to float
on water, thus assisting dispersal. The
cones remain on the trees throughout
winter and attract seed-eating birds.

A Bark, Common Alder.
B Fruit (left) and ♂ catkins, Common Alder.
C Mature ♀ catkins and leaves, Common Alder.

Betulaceae
Common Hornbeam—*Carpinus betulus* L.

Common
Hornbeam

Description
The Common Hornbeam is a sturdy, wide-spreading, deciduous tree with a superficial resemblance to the European Beech. Its dimensions vary considerably depending on the type and fertility of the soil. At best it is a small tree 6–24 m high, with a girth of 2–3 m. The trunk is fluted and elliptical, rather than round, in cross-section, bearing long, ascending branches which droop at their extremities and are lighter and more numerous than those of beech. It is often coppiced or pollarded, and has a life-span of about 150 years.

Timber
White, very hard, tough, close grained, but will not take a polish. Used extensively in the past for mill wheel cogs, rollers, and cattle yokes. Used today in chopping blocks, skittles, piano parts and certain tools. It makes excellent fuel.

Range and Habitat
Native to Asia Minor, temperate Europe and introduced to N. America. In Britain planted up to N. Scotland but indigenous only to parts of southern England and Wales. The Hornbeam thrives best on strong, rich, porous land and is tolerant of shade and moderate air pollution.

Related Trees
The North American Hornbeam or Blue Beech, *C. caroliniana* Walt., introduced to Europe, has hairy winter buds and silky reddish-tinged twigs. In autumn the leaves turn scarlet and orange. The Eastern Hornbeam, *C. orientalis* Mill., and the Japanese Hornbeam, *C. japonica* Bl., are occasional introductions to N. European parks and gardens. They both have small leaf-like, sharply dentate, unlobed fruit bracts.

Associated Macro-fungi
Terrestrial—*Lactarius circellatus* Fries; *Leccinum carpini* (R. Schulz.) Reid.

Associated Insects
Lepidoptera—Moths: *Phyllonorycter carpinicolella* Staint., larvae mine on upperside of leaf. *P. tenella* Zell., larvae mine underside of leaves. **Diptera**—Gall midge: *Zygobia carpini* Loew, forms swellings on midrib.

General Information
All species are suitable for gardens or roadside planting, and being slow growing and hardy they are ideal for hedges. The English name appears to have been derived from either the hardness of the timber or due to the fact that cattle yokes made from this timber were attached to the horns of the animals. In bygone days when wood was a major fuel, the country people in some areas held the highly valued right of top-lopping. Because of its value as firewood the Hornbeam suffered much in consequence, especially in Epping Forest where the tree is fairly common. When the forest eventually became public property, those holding this cutting right were compensated for any loss they incurred as a result.

Bark: Smooth, in varying shades and patterns of grey or greyish-brown.

Twigs: Slender, greyish-brown and sparsely hairy. The buds, unlike those of beech, are short and adpressed, with brown scales and pubescent tips.

Leaves: Unfold April–May. Alternate, shortly petiolate, elliptical-ovate with pointed apex, 5–7.5 cm long, margin finely and sharply double serrate. The parallel veins appear pleated. Autumn tints yellow to gold. Lower leaves of trees and those on hedges are often retained throughout winter.

Flowers: Develop as leaves appear. Monoecious, anemophilous. Male catkins always pendant, 2.5–7 cm long, yellowish-green, abundant and set below sharp-tipped oval bracts; they shed pollen and soon fall. Female catkins are pendant after fertilisation and carry small green flowers set in pairs, shielded by small bracts which soon disappear and are superseded by 3-lobed, leafy bracteoles which enlarge enormously throughout the summer.

Fruit: An ovoid nut, ribbed lengthwise, about 7 mm long at the base of the 3-lobed bracteole. Brown when ripe in October and November.

A Bark, Common Hornbeam.
B Catkins ♂ (left) and ♀ (right), Common Hornbeam.
C Fruit and leaves, Common Hornbeam.

Betulaceae
Hazel or Cobnut—*Corylus avellana* L.

Hazel

Description
The Hazel is usually seen as a coppiced, deciduous bush and even when allowed to develop freely from the outset, never becomes a great tree. One of the largest ever recorded in Britain was 18.5 m high but generally it averages only 5–6 m and is rarely single-stemmed. The life-span is between 70 and 80 years.

Timber
White to reddish, soft yet tough and flexible. Of no account for structural purposes but used, especially in past, for cask hoops, walking-sticks, hurdles, thatching spars, etc. The forked twigs are used as divining rods.

Range and Habitat
Native to Europe including Britain, western Asia, and N. Africa. Common on base rich and neutral substrates, but does not flourish on acid soils.

Related Trees
The variety 'Contorta' has twigs and branches which bend and twist in all directions. The Turkish Hazel, C. *colurna* L., is a much larger tree than C. *avellana*, and a native of S.E. Europe. It has brown, fissured bark, very level branches and large obovate leaves, and is occasionally found in parks and gardens throughout Britain. The Filbert, C. *maxima* Rehd., native to S.E. Europe and western Asia, is often planted in Britain. It closely resembles the Hazel but grows to a greater size and bears longer catkins and larger leaves. The nut is contained in an elongated tubular cup and is longer and not so rounded as our native hazel nut. The Purple-leaf Filbert, C. *maxima* 'Purpurea', is a variety planted mainly for its attractive foliage.

Associated Macro-fungi
Terrestrial—*Inocybe margaritispora* (Berk.) Sacc.; *Leccinum (Boletus) carpini* (R. Schulz.) Reid; *Lactarius pyrogalus* (Fries) Fries. **Lignicolous**—

Sarcoscypha coccinea Sacc., Scarlet Elf-cup; *Marasmius foetidus* Fries; and *Mycena polygramma* (Bull. ex Fries) Kumm., on dead branches, twigs and stumps.

Associated Insects
Lepidoptera—Moths: *Phyllonorycter coryli* Nicelli, larvae mine upperside of leaves. *P. nicellii* Staint., larvae mine underside of leaves. *Parornix devoniella* Staint., larvae in folded edges of leaves. **Coleoptera**—Longhorn beetle: *Phytoecia cylindrica* L. Weevil: *Apoderus coryli* L. **Hymenoptera**—Sawfly: *Allantus coryli* Stritt. **Diptera**—Gall midges: *Dasyneura corylina* Kief.; *Contarinia coryli* Kaltenb., in catkins.

General Information
Planted extensively in England over large areas centuries ago and cut periodically to provide poles for various uses. Once planted it is difficult to eradicate. The nuts, being tasty and nutritious, are in demand for man, bird and beast, the two latter often assisting dispersal. The tree's name is taken from the Anglo-Saxon word 'hæesl' or 'hæesel' and signifies a staff of authority, for in those days the rods were used to drive cattle and slaves.
The lichen in our illustration of the Hazel bark is *Graphis scripta* form *serpentina*. Common in northern England and especially so in Scotland.

Bark: Smooth, shiny and greyish-brown, often peeling thinly. The numerous lenticels are light in colour.

Twigs: Flexible and tough, pale brown and covered with reddish glandular hairs. Buds bluntly avoid, pale brown, then green.

Leaves: Unfold late April and May. Cordate with pointed apex, 5–10 cm long, margin double serrate, petiole short and stout. Young leaves are pubescent and soft, later coarsely glabrous. Autumn tint yellow.

Flowers: Monoecious, anemophilous, usually maturing in January or February. Male catkins, 'lambs' tails', are pendulous, 2–7 cm long; at first bright yellow with pollen, soon becoming dowdy and falling. Female flowers, often difficult to see, are sub-sessile and small, 5 mm long, bud-like with crimson styles.

Fruit: Each fertile female flower develops into clusters of 1–4 whitish-green, flatly ovoid nuts, enclosed in a leafy lacerate cupule. By October they are brown, ripe and edible.

A Bark and lichen (*Graphis scripta*), Hazel.
B Catkins ♂ and flowers ♀, Hazel.
C Fruit and leaves, Hazel.

Fagaceae
European Beech—*Fagus sylvatica* L.

European Beech (open grown)

Description
The mature Beech tree assumes different forms according to its situation. When close grown in a forest it is straight and pillar-like, unbranched for a height of 15 m or more. In open parkland it becomes a huge squarish tree, with wavy and almost horizontal lower branches which often spread very widely at head height from a massive buttressed bole. A good Beech will attain a height of between 30 and 35 m, and exceptionally up to 50 m; a girth of 6 m is not uncommon. Under favourable circumstances it will thrive for 200 years or more, but by this time it is usually infected by parasitic fungi and has become hollow-hearted.

Timber
White, sometimes reddish when grown on very rich soils; exceedingly heavy when newly felled but loses around 25% of its weight on drying out. Close grained, smooth and hard, not very durable for outside use, but very durable under water. Suitable for plain furniture, tool handles and many other wooden domestic articles. Burns well. Bark sometimes used for basket-work and band-boxes.

Range and Habitat
Native to Europe and the southern half of England and Wales; introduced to most other parts of Britain. The Beech thrives best on well-drained, base-rich soils, and dislikes heavy clays or very acid substrates. Its roots are substantial and spreading but remain close to the surface.

Related Trees
The Copper Beech 'Purpurea', and the Cut-leaf or Fern-leaf Beech, 'Heterophylla', are attractive varieties of the typical form.

Associated Macro-fungi
Terrestrial—*Amanita citrina* var. *alba* Gill.; *Boletus edulis* Fries; *Collybia fuscopurpurea* (Fries) Kumm.; *Coprinus picaceus* (Fries) S. F. Gray; *Cortinarius pseudosalor* J. Lange; *Hygrophorus chrysaspis* Métrod; *Lactarius blennius* (Fries) Fries; *Marasmius cohaerens* (Fries) Cooke & Quél.; *Russula alutacea* (Fries) Fries; *R. fellea* (Fries) Fries; *R. mairei* Sing.; *R. virescens* (Zant.) Fries. **Lignicolous**—*Oudemansiella mucida* (Fries) Höhn.; *Ganoderma applanatum* (Fries) Karst.; *G. europaeum* Stey.; *Bulgaria inquinans* Fries; *Xylosphaera polymorpha* (Merat) Dumort.

Associated Insects
Lepidoptera—Moth: *Stauropus fagi* L., Lobster Moth, larvae feed openly on leaves. **Coleoptera**—Beetles: *Lucanus cervus* L., Common Stag Beetle; *Sinodendron cylindricum* L.; *Dorcus parallelopipedus* L.; *Melolontha melolontha* L., Cockchafer. Weevil: *Orchestes fagi* L., Beech Leaf Miner Weevil. **Homoptera**—Aphid: *Phyllaphis fagi* L., causes galls and leaf distortion. Scale insect: *Cryptococcus fagi* Barensp., Felted Beech Coccus, often evidenced by the presence of a thick felt of white wool on the bark. **Diptera**—*Hartigiola annulipes* Hart.; *Mikiola fagi* Hart., cause leaf galls.

General Information
Large, old beech trees have a tendency to shed heavy branches when in full leaf, particularly in windy weather coinciding with heavy rain. The Beech is a useful tree for mixed woods or shelter belts but is not recommended for the small garden or close to buildings. It affords deep shade; very few plants will survive beneath its canopy. 'Pannage' was the custom of taking pigs to beech or oak woods to feed on the fruits.

Bark: Metallic grey and smooth, sometimes cracking vertically.

Twigs: Long, slender and zig-zag in outline owing to the fact that the

European Beech (close grown)

narrow, pointed leaf buds are set on alternate sides of the stem. Buds covered with chaffy brown stipules which quickly fall away as the leaves expand.

Leaves: Unfold April and May. Broadly ovate and pointed, with a somewhat scalloped margin. 4–9 cm long. At first translucent emerald green, fragile and pubescent, fringed with silvery, silky hairs; very soon thickening, becoming darker and glabrous. Petiole short. In early autumn the dark green leaves turn russet and brown and are shed; excepting those of very young trees and beech hedges, which are retained until the following spring.

Flowers: April and May, after leaves. Monoecious, anemophilous. Male catkins long stalked, containing up to 15 flowers; each flower consists of a tiny brown cup densely covered with silvery hairs and has 8 or more yellow stamens hanging from it. Female flowers, usually 2 together, each having 3 styles, are enclosed in a cup-like structure of overlapping scales, with the styles projecting at the apex. Male flowers soon fall to the ground, but the females, once pollinated, produce seed vessels.

Fruit: Brown, rounded base covered with hooked bristles, soft at first, but by autumn has become hard and rough. When ripe the box splits four ways, releasing one or two 3-sided nuts or fruits, generally referred to as 'beech-mast'. They are smooth and brown with a white kernel.

A Bark, European Beech.
B Flowers ♂, European Beech.
C Fruit and leaves, European Beech.

Fagaceae
Sweet or Spanish Chestnut—*Castanea sativa* Mill.

Sweet
Chestnut

Description
The Sweet Chestnut is a magnificent, sturdy tree, growing up to 30 m high with a girth of as much as 12 m. It is quick growing, producing a broad crown and massive tortuous branches which taper rather abruptly. The species is notably long-lived, especially in its native environment, and even in Britain there are living specimens over 500 years old.

Timber
The hard, rich-brown wood of younger or coppiced trees grown under favourable conditions is a very useful commodity, being strong and durable. It is used extensively for fence palings and posts, also wine casks, walking sticks and coffins. Timber from large old British trees once enjoyed a great reputation in use for structural purposes, but it is apt to be shaky (split) and is no longer popular. As a fuel it is first class. Used in the manufacture of castanets, hence its generic name *Castanea*.

Range and Habitat
Indigenous to S. and E. Europe, W. Asia, and N. Africa, but was probably introduced into Britain by the Romans. It favours a deep porous, acid soil.

Related Trees
There are ten known species to be found throughout the N. Temperate Zone, some have become very rare due to a fungal disease, similar in effect to Dutch elm disease. The closely related Golden Chinquapin, *Chrysolepis chrysophylla* (Hook.) Hjelm, is an evergreen and native to parts of the north-western USA.

Associated Macro-fungi
Several species associated with oaks may be found on or under this tree, including *Fistulina hepatica* Fries which causes a dark brown colouring of the timber.

Associated Insects
Micro-lepidoptera—*Coleophora anatipennella* Hübn., larvae make cases and feed on the leaves. *Incurvaria muscalella* F., larvae feed in mines and later on the leaves in portable cases. *Stigmella atricapella* Haworth, larvae mine leaves. **Macro-lepidoptera**—*Chloroclystis v-ata* Haworth, V.-Pug, larvae feed on blossoms. **Coleoptera**—*Platypus cylindrus* F., pinhole borer in unbarked timber and stumps.

General Information
A Chestnut once grew on Mount Etna that is said to have been over 3000 years old with a girth of almost 50 m. In parts of Europe the nuts form a staple article of food and the flour obtained from them can be made into bread. It should not be planted in small gardens, but makes an ideal parkland tree.

Bark: Smooth and purplish-grey in young trees. Mature trees have bark of grey to dark brown, generally deeply ridged in uniform spirals upwards round their trunk, sometimes the ridges form a network which runs perpendicularly up the tree.

Twigs: Purplish-brown, bold and ribbed with blunt, round buds which are alternately set.

Leaves: Unfold April–May. Oblong-lanceolate, up to 25 cm long with well-defined midrib and parallel veins and boldly dentate margin. Pale green at first, becoming dark green and glabrous, then yellow to brown in autumn.

Flowers: Late June–early July. Monoecious, entomophilous. Very plentiful with male and female flowers on one erect stalk 20 cm long; the males uppermost, the females towards the base. Male flowers consist of pale yellow clusters of stamens set catkin-like. Female flowers in groups of 3 are green and bud-like, and have an unpleasant sickly scent.

Fruit: The fertile female flowers mature quickly into the familiar, mildly prickly green cupules with interior white silky hairs. Each cupule contains up to 3 shiny, deep brown nuts (chestnuts) which are fully ripe by October and are released when the outer case splits into several lobes. In British trees the fruits are usually of poor size and quality.

A Bark, Sweet Chestnut.
B Catkins ♂ and leaves, Sweet Chestnut.
C Flowers ♀, Sweet Chestnut.
D Fruit, Sweet Chestnut.

Fagaceae
Common or Pedunculate Oak—*Quercus robur* L.

Common Oak

Sessile Oak

Description
The Common Oak is a deciduous, forest-forming, light-demanding, deep and broadly rooting, windfirm tree. Growing to between 15 and 30 m in height and having a trunk diameter of between 1 and 1.5 m or more in old pollards, the size is very much dependent on soil and climatic conditions. When open grown, the bole is short and robust, usually less than 9 m long, with massive, wide-spreading, irregular and tortuous branches. Both trunk and branches often burred. The crown is broad, deep and rounded. Fully grown at 250 years, oaks may live for 1000 years, especially if pollarded early in life.

Timber
Sapwood pale brown, heartwood yellowish- to reddish-brown or dark brown, hard, strong, tough, coarse in texture and straight grained. Heartwood very durable for indoor and outdoor use, one of the best hardwoods and used extensively. Should not be in constant contact with metals owing to corrosive effect. Uses include flooring, doors, roof beams, boats, furniture, gates, fence posts, coffins, veneers. Burns well. Bark used for tanning.

Range and Habitat
Very wide distribution throughout Europe and W. Asia. Native to Britain. Prefers lowland, heavy, fertile soil.

Related Trees
The Sessile or Durmast Oak, *Q. petraea* (Mattusc.) Liebl., is very similar and the two species hybridise freely, often making identification difficult. The main difference is in the acorns which are sessile in *Q. petraea*, rather than stalked as in *Q. robur*. The Sessile Oak is usually a narrower, straighter tree, with a longer, more slender trunk and less tortuous branches. The leaves usually have 5–8 shallow lobes on each side and are wedge-shaped or cordate at base; no auricles; petiole 12–25 mm long. Female flowers on short stalks. It is also less conservative than Common Oak in choice of soils. There are several cultivars and hybrids of both oaks.

Associated Macro-fungi on European Oaks
Terrestrial—*Amanita phalloides* (Fries) Secr., Death Cap; *Hygrophorus eburneus* (Fries) Fries; *Tricholoma acerbum* (Fries) Quél.; *Leccinum quercinum* (Pilát) Green & Watl.; *Boletus albidus* Rocq.; *B. appendiculatus* Fries; *B. reticulatus* Boud.; *B. pulverulentus* Opat.; *B. versicolor* Rostk.; *Gyroporus castaneus* (Fries) Quél.; *Russula vesca* Fries; *Lactarius quietus* (Fries) Fries; *L. chrysorheus* Fries. (Continued on p. 44.)

Associated Insects on European Oaks
Lepidoptera—Butterfly: *Quercusia quercus* L., Purple Hairstreak. (Continued on p. 44.)

General Information
The oak is regarded in many countries as a symbol of great strength, endurance and majesty. The Druids planted oaks to form sacred groves in which they held courts and enacted rites. Acorns were once valued as food for swine, and galls were used in the manufacture of ink and medicines. Oaks support good undergrowth and have a very high wildlife value. They are ideal for planting in large gardens.

Bark: Smooth, grey, shiny in young trees; soon rough, grey, flecked brown. Longitudinally fissured, developing into irregular plates.

Twigs: Green to greyish-green or brownish, uneven and knobbly. Winter buds mainly clustered at shoot tips, with a few solitary buds lower down on shoots, ovoid-conic, light brown, multi-scaled, slightly 5-angled, grey-pubescent under lens.

A

Leaves: Unfold late April–May. Oblong-obovate, pinnately lobed with 4–5 fairly deep lobes each side, about 10 cm long; usually auricled at base. Pale green at first, later dark green and leathery. Petiole very short, 5–10 mm long. Young trees often retain dead leaves over winter. Autumn tints dull brown, yellow, russet, bronze or red.

Flowers: Late April–May with leaves. Monoecious, anemophilous. Male catkins slender, in pendant clusters on a single stalk, set at intervals on shoot. Each flower independent and sessile, greenish-yellow, with basal bract, 4–12 yellow stamens, 6 green sepals. Female flowers round, pale brown with red stigma, single or in groups, on long, stiff stalks in leaf axils at end of shoots.

Fruit: Ripen and fall October. Acorns seldom produced in numbers until tree over 60 years old. Each acorn is a 1-seeded ovoid nut resting in a shallow cup with a rough, scaly exterior. Cup and nut up to 3 cm long, green, ripening brown. Stalk 4–8 cm long.

B

A Bark, Common Oak.
B Catkins ♂, Common Oak.
C Acorns, Common Oak.
D Acorns, Sessile Oak.

D

C

Fagaceae
Turkey Oak—*Quercus cerris* L.

Description
The Turkey Oak is a very fast-growing deciduous tree, occasionally reaching 40 m in height. The trunk, which is not burred, is usually long and straight, as are the ascending branches which are thickened where they join the main stem. In outline the tree is narrowly pyramidal, becoming broader in old age.

Timber
Much inferior to both *Q. petraea* and *Q. robur* when grown outside southern Europe, though straighter grained and heavier. Difficult to season and subject to shake and warp. Not much used in northern Europe other than for interior decoration and furniture; unsuitable for outdoor purposes.

Range and Habitat
Native to southern and central Europe, and S.W. Africa, introduced to Britain in 1735 where it is now common in parks and gardens, woods and hedgerows. Hardy throughout the country and naturalised in many localities, but never planted for timber. Prefers dry, loamy, neutral substrates in sheltered situations with a southerly aspect. A good landscape tree when given adequate space.

Turkey Oak

Related Trees
The Cork Oak, *Q. suber* L., (evergreen) is native to southern Europe and N. Africa; common in Spain and Portugal where it is grown on a semicommercial scale for its corky bark, which is part cut in sections from each mature tree every ten years or so. Introduced to S. England in 1581 or 1699 but is neither common nor hardy in northern latitudes. From a distance the tree somewhat resembles Holm Oak, but is usually shorter of stature, wider spreading, the thin branches more contorted, and the bark thick and corky, not thin and hard. *Q. x hispanica* Lam. is a natural hybrid between *Q. suber* and *Q. ilex* which occurs in

Cork Oak

Lucombe Oak

southern Europe. The form 'Lucombeana', the Lucombe Oak was first raised by William Lucombe, an Exeter nurseryman, in 1765 and has since been planted regularly in S. Britain and in Europe. The tree is sub-evergreen with varying characteristics, the old leaves fall as the new leaves unfold, the ripe acorn cups are bristly or mossy as in Turkey Oak, and take two years to mature, the bark is usually corky but not always, and the leaves very variable in extent of the lobing.

Associated Macro-fungi on European Oaks
Continued from p. 42. **Lignicolous**—*Chlorosplenium aeruginosum* (Fries) De Not., causes 'green oak timber'. *Fistulina hepatica* Fries, Beef Steak Fungus, causes 'brown oak timber'. *Laetiporus sulphureus* (Fries) Murr., Sulphur Polypore; *Daedalea quercina* Pers.; *Hymenochaete rubiginosa* (Fries) Léville; *Peniophora quercina* (Fries) Cooke; *Stereum gausapatum* (Fries) Fries; *Inonotus dryadeus* (Fries) Murr., causes white soft rot in the butt of the tree; *Mycena inclinata* (Fries) Quél.; *Psathyrella obtusata* (Fries) A.H. Sm.

Associated Insects on European Oaks
Continued from p. 42. Moths: *Peridea anceps* Goeze, Great Prominent; *Dichonia aprilina* L., Merveille-du-Jour; *Dryobotodes eremita* F., Brindled Green; *Orthosia minosa* Denis & Schiff., Blossom Underwing; *Catocala sponsa* L., Dark Crimson Underwing; *Boarmia roboraria* Denis & Schiff., Great Oak Beauty; *Serraca punctinalis* Scop., Pale Oak Beauty; *Comibaena pustulata* Hufn., Blotched Emerald; *Agriopis leucophaearia* Denis & Schiff., Spring Usher; *Drepana binaria* Hufn., Oak Hook Tip, larvae feed on leaves. *Tortricodes alternella* Denis & Schiff.; *Tortrix viridana* L. (occasionally on other trees); *Ancylis mitterbacheriana* Denis & Schiff., larvae feed on leaves. *Phycita roborella* Denis & Schiff.;

Teleiodes paripunctella Thunb., larvae in spun leaves. (Continued on p. 46.)

General Information
Over 80% of all known species of gall wasps are associated with oaks.

Bark: Mature tree dark grey, rough and deeply fissured into longitudinal thick ridges, orange colour often apparent at the bottom of the deep fissures.

Twigs: Brownish- or greenish-grey, fairly straight and densely pubescent. Buds ovoid and brown with ciliate-pubescent scales, surrounded by long stipules springing from the base.

Leaves: Unfold May. Very variable in shape, 5–10 cm long, oblong or obovate; lobes usually deep, 6–9 each side, unequal and lanceolate. Dark green and rough above, paler and woolly beneath; eventually only woolly on veins. Petiole short; stipulate. Leaves persist on the tree until winter. Autumn tints russet, brown or grey.

Flowers: With leaves, May. Monoecious, anemophilous. Male catkins in dense clusters; each catkin 5–7.5 cm long, pubescent, and brownish-yellow when in full bloom. Females on new shoots in leaf axils, singly or in small groups, each obovoid, 5 mm long, on short stalks, with yellowish scales and red stigmas.

Fruit: Usually ripening brown in second year, a sessile acorn 2–3 cm long, narrowly ovoid, minutely tomentose at apex, solitary or 2 together; cup hemispherical, exterior bristly with dense, moss-like scales.

A Bark, Turkey Oak.
B Leaves and buds with stipules, Turkey Oak.
C Acorns, Turkey Oak.

Fagaceae
American Red Oak—*Quercus rubra du Roi*

American Red
Oak

Description
The American Red Oak is a rapid-growing and colourful deciduous tree which quickly matures into a broadly domed tree up to 30 m high. It has a short, straight bole with long, straight and slightly ascending branches. The species is not long-lived by oak standards, about 200 years would seem to be its normal life-span in Europe.

Timber
Heartwood reddish, coarse grained, porous and difficult to work. Not very durable, suitable only for indoor use in joinery and furniture, etc. Inferior to timber from indigenous British oaks. Burns well. Bark used for tanning.

Range and Habitat
Native of eastern N. America, introduced to Britain and Europe in the 18th century. Now commonly found in parkland, gardens and on roadsides, also in mixed forests for timber. It is a very adaptable and hardy tree which will thrive in most substrates.

Related Trees
The Pin Oak, *Q. palustris* Muench., and the Scarlet Oak, *Q. coccinea* Muench., also introduced to Europe from N. America, are both similar to American Red Oak and as hardy. There are hundreds of oak species and hybrids native throughout the northern hemisphere, many of which have been successfully introduced to countries in the southern hemisphere.

Associated Macro-fungi
Many species listed for European oaks probably occur with introduced American species.

Associated Insects on European Oaks
Continued from p. 45. This list is continued here under American Red Oak due to limited space available. Although many of these insects have been found on introduced oaks in Europe, we do not intend to convey that this is commonplace. *Pammene argyrana* Hübn., larvae on oak galls. *Cydia splendana* Hübn., larvae on acorns. *Dystebenna stephensi* Staint., on bark. *Diurnea phryganella* Hübn., larvae in folded leaf. *Coleophora flavipennella* Dupon., larvae in pale, short cylindrical case on underside of leaf. *Phyllonorycter roboris* Zell., larvae mine leaves. *Tischeria ekebladella* Bjerk.; *Dyseriocrania subpurpurella* Haworth, larvae in blotch mines on leaves. *Stigmella atricapella* Haworth, larvae in long, sinuous leaf mines. Oaks are often partially defoliated by larvae of *Erannis defoliaria* Clerck, Mottled Umber; and by *Opherophtera brumata* L., Winter Moth, but these will both feed also on other trees. **Coleoptera**—Leaf beetles: *Crytocephalus querceti* Suff., adult feeds on leaves. Longhorn beetles: *Prionus coriaceus* L.; *Clytus arietus* L.; *Leiopus nebulosus* L., larvae in dead wood (may attack other trees). Weevils: *Attelabus nitens* Scop.; *Rhynchites caeruleus* DeGeer, larvae feed on roots, adults on foliage. *Curculio villosus* F.; *C. venosus* Grav., eggs laid in acorns, larvae feed on acorns. Bark beetles: *Scolytus intricatus* Ratz.; *Dryocoetes villosus* F., feed on bark. *Xestobium rufovillosum* DeGeer, Death Watch Bettle, larvae and adults feed in wood. Powder-post beetles: *Lyctus brunneus* Steph., feed in dead wood. (All the above mentioned bark and wood beetles may attack other trees.) **Homoptera**—Aphids: *Myzocallis castanicola* Baker; *Tuberculatus querceus* Kaltenb.; *T. annulatus* Hart.; *T. neglectus* Krzy. (recorded from *Q. petraea*), may cause distortion or galls. Leaf-hoppers: *Trioza remota* Foerst.; *Ledra aurita* L. **Hymenoptera**—Sawflies: *Pamphilus sylvarum* Steph., larvae in rolled leaf. *Arge rustica* L., larvae feed on leaves. *Fenusa pygmaea* Klug, larvae mine leaves. Gallflies: *Biorhiza pallida* Oliv., forms oak apple galls in summer, root galls in winter. *Andricus fecundator*

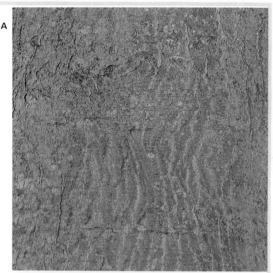

Hart., forms artichoke galls in late summer, catkin galls in spring. *A. kollari* Hart., forms marble galls, emerges in spring. *Synergus clandestinus* Eady, forms galls inside acorns, which may become distorted. *Neuroterus quercusbaccarum* L., forms spangle galls on leaves. *Cynips quercusfolii* L., forms cherry galls on leaves. Gall wasps: *Callirhytis erythrocephala* Giraud; *C. erythrostoma* Giraud, larvae in acorns of *Q. cerris*. More than 30 gall formers occur on oak. **Diptera**—Gall midges: *Macrodiplosis dryobia* Loew; *M. volvens* Kief., larvae cause leaf margins to roll inwards.

Bark: Smooth and grey in young trees; mature trees silvery or brownish-grey, shallowly and vertically fissured, underbark between fissures rich brown.

Twigs: Stout, knobbly, glabrous, and olive brown, later becoming darker. Buds ovoid and reddish-brown.

Leaves: Unfold May–June. Very variable, ovate or obovate in outline, 12–25 cm long, width of leaf and depth of lobing not constant; lobes culminating in whiskery teeth, but can also be acute and singly pointed. At first yellow then dull green. Petiole stout, and reddish at base. Autumn tints striking in orange, scarlet, dull red, yellow or brown.

Flowers: May–June. Monoecious, anemophilous. Male catkins 5–8 cm long, yellow in clusters. Females very small, ovoid and red, in leaf axils of new shoots.

Fruit: An acorn, ripens reddish-brown in October of second year, 1.8 cm long. Cup shallow with involute rim, on a short thick peduncle; scales small and closely adpressed.

A Bark, American Red Oak.
B Catkins ♂ (faded), American Red Oak.
C Acorns, American Red Oak.

Fagaceae
Holm or Evergreen Oak—*Quercus ilex* L.

Holm Oak

Description
This evergreen species of oak is usually a smallish, sombre but handsome, densely foliated tree. It is often multi-stemmed or has a very short, substantial trunk which branches out very close to the ground. Slow-growing and long-lived, it usually grows to about 6–15 m in height, but if single-stemmed may reach 30 m. The tree is often as broad as it is tall, with branches ascending, the upper ones quite steeply, to produce a very broad, round or squarish crown. It has long tap roots with very few lateral roots.

Timber
Sapwood and heartwood pale brown to reddish with conspicuous silver grain, very strong, hard and durable; takes a high polish but difficult to season and subject to split and warp. Owing to the short length of clean trunks, uses are limited. Suitable for gates, fences, vine props, furniture, decorative, and wheelright's work. Bark used for tanning and dyeing. Wood burns well and makes excellent charcoal.

Range and Habitat
Native to N. Africa and southern Europe; introduced elsewhere in Europe and the British Isles in the early 16th century. Often planted on roadsides and in parks or gardens, especially in the southern parts of England, but never for its timber. Tolerant of air pollution, does well in coastal areas not being adversely affected by salt-laden winds; but thrives best in sheltered situations on deep, fairly dry loams.

Related Trees
Turner's Oak, *Q.* × *turneri* Willd., is a hybrid between *Q. ilex* and *Q. robur*, occasionally planted in parks and gardens, a sub-evergreen tree, short in stature but well proportioned, bearing heavy, tortuous branches, and rather long, narrow leaves with a wedge-shaped base, and acute, forward-pointing teeth. Fruit similar to those of Holm Oak but on long stalk.

Associated Macro-fungi
Those listed for Common Oak probably occur with Holm Oak, especially the lignicolous species.

Associated Insects
Coleoptera—Beetles: *Lyctus* spp., Powder-post Beetles, often attack the sapwood of this and other oaks. Many of the insects listed for Common Oak are likely to occur with Holm Oak. **Homoptera**—Aphid: *Myzocallis schreiberi* Hille Ris Lambers & Stroyan.

General Information
Sometimes called Holly Oak because the leaves superficially resemble those of the Holly, this is the largest broad-leaved, fully evergreen tree growing in Britain. The fruits are said to differ in taste from tree to tree, or even on the same tree; some are sweet others bitter. It casts a dense shade, supporting no green flora at all but makes a good landscape tree.

Bark: Thin, neat, greyish-brown to dull black, broken into many small rough and irregular squarish plates.

Twigs: Slender, dull greyish-brown, and densely tomentose in the first year; then almost glabrous. Buds pale brownish and very small.

Leaves: Evergreen, each leaf remaining around 3 years, unless burned off by persistent severe frosts in extreme winters, when trees are sometimes killed. Leaves of the year unfold in June. Very variable, elliptical, ovate, oblong or lanceolate, 3–7.5 cm long, entire or serrate, even spiny, especially on very young trees. At first silvery-white and densely pubescent; later leathery, dark glossy green, glabrous above, paler and pubescent beneath. Petiole 1–2 cm long, hoary; stipules linear, purplish.

Flowers: With new leaves in June.

Monoecious, anemophilous. Male catkins
2.5–6.5 cm long, in clusters, each flower
sessile, greenish becoming yellowish.
Females greenish, from leaf axils, in
groups of 1–6 on stout tomentose stalks.

Fruit: Ripen brown and fall in October.
A sessile acorn up to 2 cm long; cup
deep, erect; exterior grey-velvety with
slightly adpressed scales.

A Bark, Holm Oak. B Leaves, Holm Oak.
C Acorns, Holm Oak.

49

Ulmaceae
Wych or Scots Elm—*Ulmus glabra* Hudson

Description
The Wych Elm is a handsome, well-proportioned deciduous tree, 24–37 m high when mature with a short, but very substantial trunk of up to 9 m in girth. When open grown, the trunk diverges into two or more long, ascending branches to form a broad, round crown. The lightest of the lower branches ascend and then arch downwards. The tree is mature at around 150 years old but is said to reach 600 years on occasion. It often carries burrs and sprouts on its trunk.

Timber
Pale to dark brown, hard and tough, flexible when steamed, non-splitting and very durable under wet or dry conditions, although subject to warp. Used in making coffins, furniture, certain parts of boats, bridges, piles, tool handles, wheelbarrows etc.; burred timber often used for panelling and cabinet-work. Considered inferior to the timber of the Common Elm.

Wych Elm

Range and Habitat
Indigenous throughout Europe and western Asia, found in parts of N. America as an introduction. In the British Isles it is commonest north of the Midlands. Grows naturally in hedgerows, woods and by water, and is not particular in its choice of substrate. Hardy against frost, wind and air pollution; more resistant to Dutch elm disease than *U. procera* or *U. carpinifolia*.

Related Trees
The variety 'Camperdown' is the common weeping elm with tortuous branches and variety 'Pendula' is semipendulous with foliage set in a herringbone pattern; both are grafts on *U. glabra* stock. The Dutch Elm *U.* × *hollandica* Mill. 'Hollandica', and the Huntingdon Elm, *U.* × *hollandica* Mill. 'Vegata', are presumed hybrids between *U. glabra* and *U. minor*.

Dutch Elm

Associated Macro-fungi on *Ulmus* spp.
Lignicolous—*Lyophyllum ulmarius* (Fries) Kühn.; *Rhodotus palmatus* (Fries) Maire; *Volvariella bombycina* (Fries) Sing.; *Polyporus squamosus* Fries; *Rigidoporus ulmarius* (Fries) Imaz. The latter two cause heart-rot and are indicative of sickly trees.

Associated Insects
See Common Elm.

General Information
In the Middle Ages long-bows were often made from the wood of this tree, which was then referred to as Witch-hasell; 'wych' meaning supple. The tough bark from young trees was once used in strips for securing thatch. Some elms have a tendency to shed branches without warning, often on windless days in high summer. Elm leaves were once highly valued as cattle fodder; they are capable of inflicting a sting similar to that of a nettle. Chests and provision boxes made from elm timber were known as 'wyches' or 'hucches'.

Bark: Smooth and grey when young; slowly becoming longitudinally furrowed and greyish-brown. In old age brown and flaky.

Twigs: Stout, dark reddish-brown and pubescent up to third year. Leaf buds narrow, pointed and brown with rusty hairs; flower buds bulky and rounded.

Leaves: Unfold April–May. Alternate, obovate, large, 7.5–15 cm long, up to 7.5 cm broad, apex abruptly pointed, margin double and treble serrate. Very rough above, pubescent beneath, with 15 or more pairs of main veins. Almost sessile, unequal at base, the longer side forming a lobe which all but obscures the short, hairy petiole. Autumn tint golden yellow.

Flowers: Before leaves, February and March. On the bare twigs in dense bunches surrounded by brownish bracts, each consists of 2 styles

surrounded by a minute campanulate
perianth and 4 or 5 stamens with
purple anthers. The ovary is 2-celled,
flat and green.

Fruit: Ripen late May–June, in clusters.
A 1-seeded samara, broadly ovate and
about 2.5 cm across, glabrous and wavy-
edged with a small notch at the end.
The seed is situated centrally. Vivid
green at first then brown and scaly,
dispersed by the wind.

A Bark, Wych Elm. **B** Flowers, Wych Elm.
C Leaves and fruit, Wych Elm.

Ulmaceae
Common, English or Small-leaved Elm—*Ulmus procera* Salisb.

Common Elm

Description
The Common Elm is one of the tallest and most vigorous of the European deciduous trees, occasionally reaching 40 m in height with girths of up to 7.5 m. Typically it is single- and straight-stemmed with rather sparse but substantial ascending branches which are densely twiggy at their extremities. The crown is narrow in relation to height and the tree often has an irregular, segmented outline. The trunk is commonly burred, often with attendant sprouts, and suckers are freely produced. The Elm is mature at around 150 years old, but may live to more than double this period.

Timber
As Wych Elm but more popular in use.

Range and Habitat
Origin somewhat obscure. Possibly introduced into Britain by the Romans or perhaps a hybrid. Until recently it was a very common hedgerow or field tree of the Midlands and S. England, but in recent years its numbers have been greatly depleted by Dutch elm disease, *Ceratocystis ulmi* (Buisman) C. Moreau, an internal fungal infection carried from tree to tree by two beetle species of the genus *Scolytus*. The infection is also transmitted by root grafts.

Related Trees
The Smooth-leaved Elm, *U. minor* Mill., is most common in S.E. England and in Europe. The leaves are bright shiny green above with downy axils beneath; petiole 6–12 mm long; under 15 pairs of main veins. The Guernsey, Jersey or Wheatley Elm, *U. minor* var. *stricta* 'Sarniensis' and the Cornish Elm, *U. minor* var. *stricta* 'Cornubiensis', are possibly both native to S. and S.W. Britain. They have conical crowns and straight, rather light, steeply ascending branches. Impressive trees when mature, *U. minor* varieties have been extensively planted on roadsides throughout most of Britain from Victorian times until the latest disastrous outbreak of Dutch elm disease.

Associated Macro-fungi
See Wych Elm.

Associated Insects on Ulmus spp.
Lepidoptera—Butterflies: *Nymphalis polychloros* L., Large Tortoiseshell; *Strymonidia w-album* Knoch, White Letter Hairstreak, larvae feed on leaves. Moths: *Abraxas sylvata* Scop., Clouded Magpie; *Cosmia trapezina* L., Dun-bar; *Orthosia stabilis* Denis & Schiff., Common Quaker, larvae feed on leaves. (Many other species of *Noctuidae* larvae also feed on elms.) *Oncocera formosa* Haworth, larvae in web. *Acleris boscana* F., larvae in rolled leaf. *Epinotia trimaculana* Donov., larvae in rolled leaf or in shoots. *Cydia leguminana* Lienig & Zell., larvae in decaying bark. *Teleiodes fugitivella* Zell., larvae feed on leaves. *Phyllonorycter tristrigella* Haworth, larvae in mines on underside of leaves. *Bucculatrix boyerella* Dupon., larvae in mines, later external feeders. *Stigmella viscerella* Staint.; *S. ulmivora* Fologne, larvae in leaf mines. **Coleoptera** —Beetles: *Scolytus scolytus* F.; *S. multistriatus* Marsh., apart from being vectors of Dutch elm disease, both beetles and larvae cause considerable damage to living elm timber. **Homoptera** —Aphids: *Schizoneura ulmi* L., causes puckering and swelling on half of leaf blade. *S. lanuginosa* Hart., inside pouch formed between upper and lower epidermis of leaves. *Tetraneura ulmi* L., causes conical gall with 1 or 2 peduncles from a vein on underside of leaves. (On *U. parvifolia* Jacq., the aphid *Tinocallis ulmiparvifolia* Mats.) Leaf-hopper: *Psylla ulmi* Foerst. **Hymenoptera**—

Sawflies: *Fenusa ulmi* Sund.; *Priophorus ulmi* L., larvae on leaves. **Diptera**—Gall midges: *Janetiella lemei* Kief., causes swellings on leaf veins.

General Information

In bygone days large branches and trunks of elms were hollowed out and used for piping water. Elms are often very difficult to identify with certainty, even within a species there are many variants, and added to this, hybridisation is a regular occurrence.

Bark: Brown, rough and corky, with deep vertical fissures, resolving into plates with age.

Twigs: Pubescent when young, not so stout as those of Wych Elm. Leaf buds brown, hairy, small and pointed.

Leaves: Unfold April–May. Alternate, variably ovate, 5–7.5 cm long with abruptly pointed apex, unequal at the base, the longer side does not obscure the petiole as in the Wych Elm, margin serrate, main veins under 15 pairs. Rough above, pubescent or almost glabrous beneath. Autumn tint golden yellow.

Flowers: Appear before leaves and are very similar to those of Wych Elm although smaller.

Fruit: Sets April and May, usually sterile and rarely ripens. A 1-seeded, round samara with terminal notch.

A Bark, Common Elm.
B Leaves and fruit, Common Elm.
C Leaves, Smooth-leaved Elm.

Moraceae
Fig—*Ficus carica* L.

Fig

Description
The Fig is a small, deciduous tree which can grow up to 9 m high but is more often half that height. It has unpredictable, sturdy, upswept branches and a spreading, open crown, and often produces many suckers.

Timber
Unsubstantial, tough and porous. Of no commercial value.

Range and Habitat
Native to W. Asia, long cultivated in southern Europe and parts of the USA for its fruit crop. Possibly introduced to Britain first by the Romans but then disappeared to be re-introduced by Cardinal Pole in 1525. Now common in S.E. England in parks and gardens or in the wild as an escape; rarer in northern counties but more frequent than generally supposed.

Related Trees
A member of the mulberry family, a tropical and subtropical group of which there are about 1000 species.

Associated Macro-fungi
None specific.

Associated Insects
Homoptera—Leaf-hopper: *Homotoma ficus* L.

General Information
Dried fruits are eaten extensively in southern Europe. A laxative syrup is made from the juice, and mashed figs can be made into poultices for boils, septic wounds etc. The fresh juice from the leaves is said to cure warts. When planted it should be in a sheltered spot against a south or south-west facing wall.

Bark: Smooth, pale grey with a pattern of darker lines.

Twigs: Very stout, ribbed and dark green with prominent leaf-scars. Buds large, terminal, light green and acutely conical, laterals short, wide and purplish-brown.

Leaves: Unfold May–June. Alternate, very variable, large, 7.5–15 cm long, 6.5–19 cm broad, palmately 3- to 7-lobed, 5-partite or entire, base cordate. Texture thick, dark green and rough above, paler and hairy beneath, bluntly serrate in part, veins very prominent. Petiole stout and up to 10 cm long; stipules caducous. Autumn tint yellow.

Flowers: May–June. Monoecious, generally protogynous, but not necessarily entomophilous. Minute and unisexual, hidden and enclosed in a fleshy pear-shaped receptacle which has a small short tunnel at the apex. Male flowers near the opening; female flowers in lower part.

Fruit: A development of the receptacle together with perianth of the small flowers. Dark green at first and about 2 cm long in the autumn, growing and ripening the following year through brown to purple or blackish, and from 5 to 7.5 cm long. Esculent.

Common Mulberry—*Morus nigra* L.

Common Mulberry

Description
The Common Mulberry is a small, slow-growing, long-lived, deciduous tree, 3–9 m high and often leaning. It has a large, rounded head and stout, horizontal branches.

Timber
Sapwood white, heartwood yellowish-brown, darker when seasoned. Hard, heavy, and tough in texture. Rare and unsubstantial, but useful for inlays, ornamental work, and turning.

Range and Habitat
Native to W. Asia, supposedly introduced to Britain in early 16th century. Fairly common in parks and gardens of S. England, rare in north.

Associated Macro-fungi
None known to be specific.

Associated Insects
None in Britain. *Bombyx mori* L., Silk Moth, larvae feed on leaves.

Bark: Rough, burred and reddish-brown.

Twigs: Green, becoming brown, pubescent. Buds ovoid-conical, alternate.

Leaves: Unfold May. Ovate, cordate, sometimes 3- to 5-lobed, 7.5–10 cm long, margin coarsely serrate. Dark green, rough and hairy above, light green and pubescent beneath. Petiolate and stipulate. Autumn tint yellow.

Flowers: May. Dioecious or monoecious, anemophilous. In short, dense, greenish, catkin-like spikes.

Fruit: Ripen August–October. Female flowers form into a tight cluster of drupes, rather like a raspberry, green at first, then red, finally tinged black when they are esculent.

A Fruit and leaf, Fig.
B Cross-section of fruit, Fig.
C Fruit and leaf, Common Mulberry.

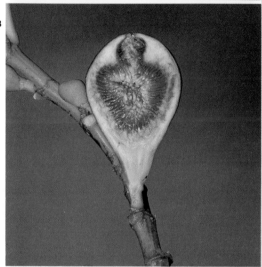

Platanaceae
London Plane—*Platanus* x *hispanica* Muench.

Description
The London Plane is a vigorous, hardy, windfirm, deciduous tree which can reach heights of over 30 m with girths of over 6 m. When open grown and not subject to lopping, the tree is beautifully proportioned, having a long, clean (though sometimes heavily burred), erect trunk, and a tall, round, open crown. The tortuous and often irregular branches are pendulous at the extremities. It is long-lived, often exceeding 300 years in Europe.

Timber
Pale yellow to light red or dark brown, fairly hard, reasonably tough and elastic, with uniform texture, but not durable outdoors. A very useful and beautiful wood used for joinery, doors, floor blocks, furniture, veneers, decorative carving, and turnery etc. When cut in a certain manner, the wood displays a silver grain referred to as lacewood.

London Plane

Range and Habitat
A tree of doubtful origin but generally regarded as a hybrid between the Oriental Plane, *P. orientalis*, and the Western Plane, *P. occidentalis*. Known in Britain since 1670, some trees planted about that time are still healthy and vigorous. Frequent in southern England, less common in Wales and north of Cheshire. On the mainland of Europe it is popular and planted throughout most suitable areas. Light loving but undemanding as to substrate; thriving in soils which are neither highly alkaline nor too heavy. Very tolerant of air pollution.

Related Trees
The Oriental Plane, *P. orientalis* L., native to S.E. Europe and Asia Minor, is very similar to London Plane, but usually carries more 'bobbles' on each stalk, the leaves are more deeply cut, and have narrow, somewhat parallel-sided lobes. Rare in Britain but popular

Oriental Plane

and often planted in its native lands. The Western Plane or Buttonwood, *P. occidentalis* L., is native to N. America, where it attains great proportions. Being subject to frost damage in Britain it rarely survives for long and is seldom planted.

Associated Macro-fungi
None specific.

Associated Insects
Homoptera—Aphids: *Drepanosiphum platanoides* Schrank; *Periphyllus testudinaceus* Fern. **Hymenoptera**—Sawflies: *Fenusa recta* Thomson; *Heterarthrus aceris* Kaltenb., larvae on leaves. (These are also found on *Acer* spp.)

General Information
The first reference to a plane tree in Britain was made by Dr William Turner in his *Herball* in 1551. Roman orators and statesmen would return home from work at midday just to feed their plane trees with wine. The great commander Xerxes stopped his army of nearly two million men just to admire a certain plane tree, then covered it in precious metals and gems. Being host to very few harmful insects and diseases, able to withstand considerable pruning and lopping, and tolerant of air pollution, it makes a popular town tree, as a stroll round London or Paris will prove. Although easily propagated by cuttings, it is not recommended for the small garden.

Bark: Grey or brown and smooth, peeling off periodically (especially in autumn) in small or large flakes revealing the yellow underbark which with time changes colour and portrays an attractive variegated effect in creams, greys, greens and yellows.

Twigs: Slender and zig-zag, at first green and white-woolly, later brown. Winter buds form and are hidden in the swollen base of the leaf stalks of the year; when the leaves fall they are already formed, green and conical with a slightly curved tip.

Leaves: Unfold May. Alternate, palmately 3- to 5-lobed, very variable in size and shape from tree to tree, and even on individual trees, being up to 20 cm long, 25 cm broad. Strongly veined, pubescent at first. Petiole long and slender, and, like all maples, enlarged and hollow at the base; stipulate. Autumn tints yellow and brown.

Flowers: May. Monoecious, anemophilous. Both more or less globular (bobbles) on pendulous separate long stalks at the ends of branches. Male catkins yellowish, soon falling; female catkins red, bristly and larger than males.

Fruit: After pollination the female 'bobbles' develop into small balls, each about 2.5 cm in diameter and resembling a small burr. They turn brown and remain on the tree throughout winter. In spring the core breaks up releasing a multitude of yellow, 4-sided seeds, each with a hairy parachute at the base, these are seldom fertile. The shedding seed and leaf hairs are reputed to cause bronchial irritation in some people.

A Bark, London Plane
B Flowers ♀ London Plane.
C Leaves, London Plane.

Rosaceae
Wild Service Tree—*Sorbus torminalis* Crantz

Description
The Wild Service is a small but handsome, slow-growing tree, which usually attains a height of 9–12 m, but which occasionally grows up to 24 m high. When young, it is conical in outline, developing ascending, spreading branches and a large head when older. It is said to be a very long-lived tree.

Timber
Sapwood pale yellow, heartwood yellowish with red tint, hard, fine grained, and takes a good polish. What little is available is useful for carving, turnery and small cabinet-work.

Range and Habitat
Native to Europe including Britain, Algeria, Caucasus, and parts of the Middle East. A comparatively rare tree in the British Isles, found sparingly as far north as southern Cumbria. It thrives on heavy marl or limestone areas, in open woodland.

Wild Service Tree

Related Trees
The Service Tree of Fontainebleau, *S.* x *latifolia* (Lam.) Pers., sometimes seen as an amenity tree in parks and on roadsides, is a hybrid between *S. aria* and *S. torminalis*. The leaves are broadly ovate and rounded at the base and have sharply pointed lobes. The ripe fruits are yellow to yellowish-brown with large lenticels. The Service Tree, *S. domestica* L., should not be confused with the Wild Service. The former is native to southern Europe but not to Britain, where it is rare and found only in a few parks and gardens. It attains heights of up to 20 m and is long-living. The bark is rough and coloured in orange and brown, and the green, ovoid buds exude resin. The leaves are pinnate (not ovate) and bear similarity to those of Rowan. Fruits are large, 2–3 cm long, apple- or pear-shaped, green to brownish-red and used in Europe to make a cider-like beverage. The timber is very hard and heavy with

a reddish tint and takes a high polish.

Associated Macro-fungi
None specific in Britain.

Associated Insects
Lepidoptera—Moths: *Phyllonorycter mespilella* Hübn., larvae mine on underside of leaves. *Stigmella torminalis* Wood, larvae mine leaves. **Coleoptera**—Weevil: *Anthonomus chevrolati* Desbr. **Homoptera**—Aphid: *Dysaphis sorbi* Kaltenb.; *D. aucupariae* Buckton. **Diptera**—Gall midge: *Contarinia sorbi* Kief. (Many of these insects found on other *Sorbus* spp.)

General Information
The fruits are known as 'chequers' in S.E. England. The name Service may be derived from the Latin word 'cerevisia', meaning beer.

Bark: Adult tree grey or greyish-brown, resolving into scaly plates and shallow fissures.

Twigs: Shiny purplish-brown above, olive brown beneath; young shoots white-felted. Buds globular, shiny green; scales broad and scalloped.

Leaves: Unfold May. Alternate, very variable, maple-like, 5–10 cm long, oblong-ovate with 3–5 pairs of triangular lobes. Shiny green and glabrous above, white and woolly beneath at first, later glabrous. Petiole 2–5 cm long and pale green. Autumn tints yellow to red, or purple.

Flowers: May. Bisexual, entomophilous. White, more numerous and smaller than Whitebeam. Terminal on shoots in a loose, rounded cyme 9–12 cm across, which is covered in evanescent white down. Each flower 1 cm across with 2 styles.

Fruit: Ripen October–November. An obovoid pome about 1 cm in diameter, in long-stalked clusters. Greenish-brown to brown and dotted with lenticels. Esculent, but, like medlars, should be stored until very soft, or left on the tree until touched by frost.

A Bark, Wild Service Tree.
B Flowers, Wild Service Tree.
C Berries, Wild Service Tree.

Rosaceae
Rowan or Mountain Ash—*Sorbus aucuparia* L.

Rowan

Description
The Rowan is a small, neat and handsome tree with a straight, clean bole and light, distinctively ascending branches. It is rapid-growing, usually attaining a height of 6–12 m but occasionally up to 18 m high. Although not generally long-lived, it may survive over a century.

Timber
Pale to reddish-brown, hard, tough and elastic. Apart from small cabinet- and turnery-work it is little used. In the Middle Ages Rowan ranked second to Yew as bow-making material.

Range and Habitat
Native to all Europe, N. Africa and Asia Minor, introduced into N. America and many other parts of the world. A very hardy tree, not at all conservative in its choice of habitat; found naturally on acid- or base-rich substrates, in rocky or deep soil areas, high on mountain sides or lowland plains, in clean or heavily polluted atmospheres. Yet it is not a good mixer and quickly succumbs beneath the shade of larger tree species.

Related Trees
Within the genus *Sorbus* there are over 80 species plus many cultivars and hybrid forms, all of them colourful trees and highly recommended for roadside and garden planting. The Chinese Scarlet Rowan, *S.* 'Embley' (syn. *S. discolor* Hort.), bears orange-red berries and the leaves take on beautiful autumnal tints of red to purple. *S. hupehensis* Schneid. bears ripe berries white to pink in colour, and the leaves, at first bluish-green, turn red in autumn. These two rowans are currently very popular in western Europe.

Associated Macro-fungi
None specific.

Associated Insects
Lepidoptera: Moths: *Venusia cambrica* Curt., Welsh Wave, larvae feed on leaves. *Phyllonorycter sorbi* Frey; *P. mespilella* Hübn.; *Stigmella aucupariae* Frey; *S. nylandriella* Tengst., larvae mine leaves. *Cydia pomonella* L., Codling Moth, larvae usually feed in apples, also occur in fruits of *Sorbus* spp. **Homoptera**—Aphids: *Dysaphis aucupariae* Buckton; *D. sorbi* Kaltenb. **Hymenoptera**—Sawflies: *Pristiphora geniculata* Hart.; *Trichiosoma sorbi* Hart.; *Hoplocampa alpina* Zett., larvae on leaves. **Diptera**—Gall midge: *Contarinia sorbi* Kief., causes distortion in midrib. (Many of these insects found on other *Sorbus* spp.)

General Information
The Rowan has not the slightest affinity with the ash family. It was considered a sacred tree by the Celts. Farmers planted the trees around their dwellings and buildings to ward off witches and evil spirits, even in comparatively recent times. Although the ripe berries are non-poisonous, they are unpalatable when eaten raw. In many rural areas they are used to make wine and jelly.

Bark: Smooth, shiny and grey with darker lenticels.

Twigs: Grey to brown, pubescent when young, soon glabrous. Buds very large, long, pointed, pubescent, blackish-violet or grey.

Leaves: Unfold April. Compound-pinnate, 10–25 cm long, leaflets 9–15 including terminal, lanceolate, up to 5 cm long and deeply serrate excepting the bases which are non-serrate. Glabrous or nearly so above, paler beneath and at first densely pubescent. Petiolate. Leaf fall late October and November. Autumn tints brown, yellow and red.

Flowers: May. Bisexual, entomophilous. In dense, woolly-stemmed, creamy-white cymes, 10–15 cm across borne at the ends of short, leafy branches. Each flower about 8 mm in diameter, with 5 petals and 5 green sepals. Heavily but not pleasantly scented and visited by many insect species.

Fruit: The white petals soon fall and the fertile heart of each flower develops into a berry-like pome 6 mm in diameter, green in colour speedily changing through to bright red by August or September. The flesh is soft and orange-yellow. At this stage they are avidly devoured by various species of passerines, the seeds pass through the birds' digestive system unharmed and are spread far and wide.

A Bark, Rowan. **B** Flowers and leaves, Rowan.
C Berries, Rowan.

Rosaceae
Whitebeam—*Sorbus aria* (L.) Crantz

Whitebeam

Description
In its native habitat, this hardy, deciduous tree may attain a height of 15 m or more. The Whitebeam is erect, graceful and distinctive in its white garb, bearing upswept branches and a wide, domed crown. The young tree is conic in outline and fast-growing although the rate of growth decreases after 10 years. On poor soils and in exposed areas, the species usually makes no more than a small bush.

Timber
Sapwood pale creamy-brown, heartwood darker brown or pinkish-brown; the annual rings show up distinctly. Straight grained, fairly hard and heavy, strong and tough, takes a good polish. Not very durable for outside uses; quick seasoning causes warp. Nevertheless an excellent timber, although little is available. Useful for tool handles, bobbins, mallet heads, and small turnery, also cabinet-work, furniture, and plywood.

Range and Habitat
Native and widespread in central and southern Europe, including Britain where it is characteristic of chalk downs and limestone areas mainly in southern England.

Related Trees
There are several cultivars of Whitebeam.

Associated Macro-fungi
None specific in Britain.

Associated Insects
Lepidoptera—Moths: *Venusia cambrica* Curt., Welsh Wave; *Phyllonorycter sorbi* Frey; *P. mespilella* Hübn.; *Stigmella aucupariae* Frey; *S. nylandriella* Tengst., larvae mine leaves. **Coleoptera**—Weevils: *Rhynchites cupreus* L.; *Anthonomus consperus* Desbr. **Homoptera**—Aphids: *Dysaphis aucupariae* Buckton. **Hymenoptera**—Sawflies: *Pristiphora geniculata* Hart.; *Trichiosoma sorbi* Hart.; *Hoplocampa alpina* Zett.; *H. ariae* Benson (thought to be on *S. aria* only). **Diptera**—Gall midges: *Contarinia sorbi* Kief., causes distortion in midrib. (Many of these insects found on other *Sorbus* spp.)

General Information
In Lancashire and Cumbria the fruits are known as 'chess apples'. Local names for the tree include Hen-apple, Bean Tree, Cumberland Hawthorn, Hoar Withy, Lot-tree, Sea Owler and Wild Cowbin. The fruit is edible after being touched by frost, and is sometimes made into jam and alcoholic beverages. Whitebeam and its several cultivars are very suitable for garden, park, and street plantings, being very hardy, rootfirm, tolerant of air pollution, and attractive in appearance.

Bark: Young trees grey and smooth; older trees flaky, with shallow fissures.

Twigs: Shiny olive brown to grey, young shoots green and pubescent. Buds ovoid, large; scales green, brown at the margins, often pubescent.

Leaves: Unfold early May. Variable (there are several localised sub-species which differ from the type in shape, size, and leaf serration). Typically broadly ovate, about 8 cm long, 5 cm broad, margin irregularly serrate, or shallow lobed. Covered in dense silvery white pubescence, evanescent on the upper surface, but remains on the underside even when leaves have fallen in autumn. Petiole 1–2 cm long. Autumn tints yellowy browns and orange-scarlet.

Flowers: May–June. Bisexual, entomophilous. White, in rather loose cymes 5–8 cm across, terminal on leafy branches. Each flower 1.5 cm across, with 5 white petals, 5 green sepals and numerous stamens.

Fruit: A globular pome about 8 mm in diameter, borne in clusters; green ripening to red in September, and soon consumed and dispersed by birds.

A Bark, Whitebeam. **B** Flowers, Whitebeam.
C Berries, Whitebeam.

Rosaceae
Swedish Whitebeam—*Sorbus intermedia* (Ehrh.) Pers.

Swedish
Whitebeam

Description
The Swedish Whitebeam is a neater, more compact, deciduous tree than the related Common Whitebeam. It grows up to 10 m high and has a slender trunk bearing a dense, rounded crown.

Timber
Hard, tough, not durable and little used commercially.

Range and Habitat
Native to Scandinavia, Baltic States and N.E. Germany. Possibly introduced to Britain many years ago. Origin obscure; often said to be a cross between *S. aria* and *S. aucuparia*. A great favourite with Local Authorities, especially in industrial areas because of its resistance to air pollution, small size, compactness and capacity to thrive on most soils.

Related Trees
All *Sorbus* species hybridise freely, making identification extremely difficult. The Finnish Whitebeam, *S. hybrida* L., is a similar tree to the Swedish Whitebeam and is a hybrid between it and *S. aucuparia*. It is sometimes seen in parks and avenues. The ovate leaves are distinctive, being deeply lobed at the base, but less so at the apex. There are usually 2 pairs of free, pointed leaflets at the base and both the lobes and the leaflets are serrate at the tips. They are green above and densely greyish-white tomentose beneath. The fruits are globose and crimson when ripe. *S. x thuringiaca* is very similar to Finnish Whitebeam but the free leaflets, when present, are blunt at the tips rather than pointed. The Wild Crab Apple, *Malus sylvestris* (L.) Mill., belongs to the same family (Rosaceae) as the whitebeams and was at one time placed in the same genus under the generic name *Pyrus*. Native to Europe, including Britain, and found in hedgerows and copses, it

certainly deserves mention in this volume. It is a dense, wide-spreading tree, short in stature, growing up to 10 m high with a rounded crown and spiny branches. The brownish timber, although unsubstantial, is hard, fine grained and suitable for cabinet-work, turnery and engraving. It also burns well. The bark is dark brown and rugged, resolving into squarish plates. The twigs are reddish-brown and the mature leaves are ovate, dentate and hairless with the petiole often partly red. Flowers appear in May and are white or pinkish. The fruits are small, 2–3 cm across on long stalks, green to yellowish sometimes with a reddish flush. They are very sour but make excellent preserves. This tree is a parent of many of our orchard apples.

Associated Macro-fungi
None specific in Britain.

Associated Insects
Species found on other *Sorbus* species probably occur on this tree.

Bark: Usually smooth and purplish-grey; sometimes with shallow, scaly fissures.

Twigs: Grey or purplish-grey, tomentose only when young. Buds large, green to dark reddish-brown with grey pubescence.

Leaves: Unfold early May. Broadly elliptic, 8–12 cm long with 3–7 rounded, serrated lobes on either side, each lobe pointing slightly towards the leaf apex. Apex rather blunt and serrate. Dark shiny green above and yellowish-grey pubescent beneath.

Flowers: Late May. White, in dense, corymbose cymes which are 7–10 cm across. Each flower about 1 cm across with pale pink stamens.

Fruit: Ripen plentifully in bunches,

green to orange scarlet in September.
Each pome oblong-ovoid, 1 cm long.
Soon consumed by birds.

A Bark, Swedish Whitebeam.
B Flowers, Swedish Whitebeam.
C Berries, Swedish Whitebeam.

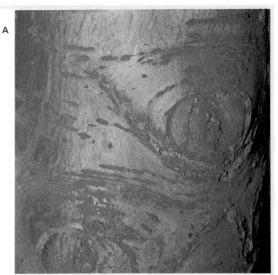

Rosaceae
Common Hawthorn—*Crataegus monogyna* Jacq.

Description
When open grown and protected against browsing animals, the Hawthorn will attain the stature of a small tree, up to 10 m high with a girth of up to 3 m. The trunk is sturdy and short, often twisted and fluted, with substantial, meandering branches, usually ascending to form a broad, round, dense, thorny crown. However, this common, tenacious, deciduous tree is more often seen in hedges, kept trimmed to fence height and periodically layered, and as a livestock barrier and shelter belt it is probably unsurpassed. It is long-lived.

Timber
Yellowish-white to pinkish and often streaky; tough, hard, and heavy when green; takes a fine polish. Useful for tool handles, walking-sticks and cabinet work. A good substitute for boxwood in engraving. Burns well and slowly.

Common Hawthorn

Range and Habitat
Native and common throughout Europe including the British Isles, where, apart from the bleakest moorland and mountainous areas, it can be seen at every turn. Thrives on all soils, windfirm, shade tolerant and good for wildlife.

Related Trees
The Midland Thorn, *C. laevigata* (Poiret) DC., is much less frequent than Common Hawthorn and prefers heavy substrates; the leaves are more bluntly lobed and mainly serrate; flowers have slightly longer petals, with 2 or 3 styles, and fruit with 2 or 3 stones. Natural hybrids occur. The attractive red, pink and double flowered trees often seen in parks and gardens are mainly cultivars of *C. laevigata*. The Cockspur Thorn, *C. crus-galli* L., is an introduced species from N. America bearing noticeably long, stout thorns and unlobed, obovate leaves which are serrate, apart from the base. They turn bright orange, red and bronze in autumn.

Cockspur Thorn

Associated Macro-fungi
Terrestrial—*Entoloma clypeatum* (Fries) Kumm. **Lignicolous**—*Pholiota squarrosa* (Fries) Kumm.; *Phellinus pomaceus* (Pers.) Maire; *P. ribis* (Schum. ex Fries) Karst.; *Stereum purpureum* (Pers.) Fries. **On fallen fruit**—*Tubaria autochthona* (Berk. & Broome) Sacc.

Associated Insects
Lepidoptera—Moths: *Allophyes oxyacanthe* L., Green-brindled Crescent; *Apatele psi* L., Grey Dagger; *Episema caerulescephala* L., Figure-of-Eight; *Euproctis similis* Fues., Yellow-tail, larvae feed on leaves. *Eriogaster lanestris* L., Small Eggar, larvae communal in webs on leaves. *Opisthograptis luteolata* L., Brimstone Moth; *Theria rupicapraria* Denis & Schiff., Early Moth, larvae feed on leaves. **Coleoptera**—Beetles: *Lochmaea crataegi* Foerst.; *Anthonomus pedicularius* L.; *Scolytus mali* Bech.; *Agrilus sinuatus* Oliv. **Homoptera**—Leaf-hoppers: *Psylla melanoneura* Foerst.; *P. peregrina* Foerst. **Hymenoptera**—Sawflies: *Hoplocampa crataegi* Klug, larvae in fruits. *Neurotoma saltuum* L., larvae in webs on leaves. *Trichiosoma tibiale* Steph.; *Arge ustulata* L., larvae on leaves. **Diptera**—True flies: *Dasyneura oxyacanthae* Rübs.; *D. crataegi* Winn.

General Information
It is said to be unlucky to have May blossom in the house, or to cut down a hawthorn tree. Henry VII adopted the hawthorn as his badge. Parkinson in 1620 wrote 'The distilled water and stone or Kernel of the Haw reduit to a powder is generally agreed to be soverain against the stone'. William Coles asserted in 1657 that powdered haws in wine are 'singularly good for the Dropsy'.

Bark: Dull grey and smooth at first; soon becoming rough and rusty-brown, breaking up into flaky rectangles.

Twigs: In a dense network. Reddish-brown then greenish-grey to black, with straight thorns. Buds small, conical; scales reddish-brown.

Leaves: Unfold March–April. Very variable in shape and size, average 2.5 cm long, simple, alternate, pinnately 3- to 5(7)-lobed, the lobes longer than their width, pointed, margin entire or scarcely serrate. Emerald green and pubescent at first, soon dark green and glabrous. Petiolate and stipulate. Autumn tints yellow, brown or crimson.

Flowers: Mid-May to mid-June. Bisexual, entomophilous. White, often pinkish later, in a dense, sessile, corymbose cyme containing upwards of 12 flowers. Each flower with 5 broad petals, 6 mm long, 5 united sepals, one style, numerous stamens with pinkish-brown anthers. Sweet to sickly scented.

Fruit: Set green in July–August, ripening red to purplish-red October–November in bunches. The familiar haw, a small, fleshy, ovoid pome bearing the remains of the sepals at the tip, and inside one hard stone.

A Bark, Common Hawthorn.
B Flowers, Common Hawthorn.
C Berries, Common Hawthorn.
D Flowers and thorns, Cockspur Thorn.

A

B

D

C

Rosaceae
Wild Cherry, Gean or Mazzard—*Prunus avium* L.

Description
The Wild Cherry is a hardy, fairly fast-growing, deciduous tree of slender habit and pyramidal outline, bearing upswept, strong and rather short, straight branches from a single bole. In parts of northern Europe it may grow to over 30 m high with a girth of 3–4 m, but it is more usually mature at 6–12 m high. Its life-span is probably 200 years at most. This is one of the most beautiful and well-proportioned trees in all seasons of the year.

Timber
Yellowish to reddish-brown, fine grained, tough and takes a fine polish. There are many uses, including cabinet-work, furniture, turnery, smokers' pipes, musical instruments, walking-sticks etc. Makes a good fuel but only when green.

Range and Habitat

Wild Cherry

Bird Cherry

Native to temperate Europe including Britain, also N. Africa and W. Asia, naturalised in parts of N. America. Thrives on most substrates but prefers base-rich soils and may be found in woods, hedgerows, parks and gardens.

Related Trees
The variety *P. avium* 'Plena' is a magnificent tree with double flowers but should only be planted in large gardens. The Sour Cherry, *Prunus cerasus* L., said to be a parent of Kentish and Morillo cherries, is a native of Asia Minor and long cultivated throughout Europe. It usually forms only a large bush and may be found naturalised in the wild. The variety *P. cerasus* 'Semperflorens' flowers at intervals in spring and summer. Both *P. cerasus* and variety 'Semperflorens' are suitable for the smaller garden. The Bird Cherry, *Prunus padus* L., native to northern and central Europe including the south of Britain, is a handsome, hardy shrub or small tree up to 15 m high, bearing fragrant white flowers in May in loose,

erect, pendulous racemes 4–14 cm long. The leaves are ovate and finely dentate. The fruit, a small globular drupe, is polished black when ripe and bitter-sweet to taste. The tree is often defoliated by larvae of the Small Ermine Moth, *Yponomeuta evonymella* L. There is a vast range of ornamental cherry trees, with flowers varying in colour between white and red; many of these are of Japanese origin.

Associated Macro-fungi
None specific. *Entoloma clypeatum* (Fries) Kumm. is regularly found beneath cherry trees.

Associated Insects
Hymenoptera—Sawfly: *Hoplocampa flava* L. (also found on Blackthorn and Sour Cherry), larvae feed on leaves.

General Information
All cultivated sweet cherries are descended from this tree, producing the fruit used in preserves, liqueurs, wines and as glacé cherries in cakes, trifles etc. In legend, the cuckoo is frequently associated with the cherry tree although there would seem to be no reasoning behind this as the cuckoo rarely eats vegetable matter.

Bark: Young trees, shiny purplish-brown with numerous prominent lighter coloured lenticels. Peels off in strips horizontally. Dark purple on older trees, especially when open grown, often splitting vertically and creating shallow fissures giving a contorted appearance.

Twigs: Stout, grey to reddish-brown. Buds alternate, reddish-brown, large and pointed.

Leaves: Unfold April–May. Broadly ovate, 5–12.5 cm long, tapering to a pointed apex, margin sharply serrate. Pale bronzy green, becoming dark green, pubescent beneath, drooping, soft; two glands at the base. Petiole long, reddish above, yellowish beneath and grooved;

stipulate. Autumn tints yellow then orange-red to crimson.

Flowers: Usually appear with leaves, occasionally before. Entomophilous, bisexual. Very profuse clusters of 2–6 snowy-white, short-stalked flowers, up to 4 cm in diameter. Petals obovate and deeply notched. Pistil and stamens mature at same time.

Fruit: Ripen July–August. A cordate drupe about 12 mm in diameter with a large stone and little flesh, hanging in bunches. Green at first then dark red, sweet or bitter. Soon stripped by birds.

A Bark, Wild Cherry. **B** Flowers, Wild Cherry.
C Cherries and leaves, Wild Cherry.

Rosaceae
Blackthorn or Sloe—*Prunus spinosa* L.

Blackthorn

Description
The Blackthorn is a freely suckering, thicket-forming, deciduous shrub or small tree up to 6 m high, although it is usually only half that height. It is very thorny, rigid and dense, the light, wiry branches being unpredictable in their direction of growth and often covered with grey lichen.

Timber
Hard and tough, takes a good polish. Owing to its small size the wood is of little use commercially but straight stems are used for making walking-sticks.

Range and Habitat
Native and widely distributed in temperate Europe including Britain; introduced and naturalised in parts of N. America. Grows almost anywhere apart from permanently damp or very acid sites, but thrives best in lime-rich areas.

Related Trees
The Bullace, *P. domestica* L. subsp. *insititia*, is similar to Blackthorn and is sometimes found in similar situations. It may be distinguished by its pubescent reddish-brown to grey twigs, fewer spines and larger leaves and fruit, which, when ripe, may be black, green, red or yellow. Blackthorn itself is not recommended for the garden, but the cultivars *P. spinosa* 'Plena', with its double white flowers, and 'Purpurea', with bronze-red leaves, are quite rewarding. Plums and damsons are closely allied to Blackthorn.

Associated Macro-fungi
Lignicolous—*Fomes pomaceus* Quél.; *Stereum purpureum* (Pers.) Fries. (The latter causes silver-leaf disease.)

Associated Insects
Lepidoptera—Butterflies and moths: *Strymonidia pruni* L., Black Hairstreak, larvae on leaves. *Gelechia scotinella*

Herr.-Schaeff., larvae in spun flowers. *Dichomeris fasciella* Hübn., larvae in folded leaves. *Enicostoma lobella* Denis & Schiff., larvae in web beneath leaves. *Argyresthia albistria* Haworth, larvae in shoots. *Pseudoswammerdamia caesiella* Hübn.; *Yponomeuta padella* L., larvae in web on leaves. *Coleophora anatipennella* Hübn., larvae in cylindrical case on leaves. **Coleoptera** —Beetles: *Magdalis ruficornis* L.; *M. cerasi* L., in dead branches. **Diptera**— Gall midges: *Dasyneura tortrix* L., in thickened shoots.

General Information
The leaves were at one time added to tea as an adulterant. The ripe berries can be made into a preserve, used to flavour and colour gin, or fermented into a wine called winter pick (sometimes known as 'sloe poison'!). Gilbert White, in his *Natural History of Selborne*, remarked 'This tree usually blossoms while cold north-east winds blow; so that the harsh rugged weather obtaining at this season is called by the country people—blackthorn winter.' Blackthorn is often seen in hedgerows along with Hawthorn, but is not regarded as good hedging material on its own.

Bark: Thin and black, becoming rough when old (illustration shows very new wood). It is astringent and has been used for tanning leather and manufacturing ink.

Twigs: Reddish-brown, pubescent; very soon black, glabrous, rigid, spiny and much-branched. Buds minute; scales reddish-brown, almost glabrous.

Leaves: Unfold late April–May. Alternate, ovate or elliptical, 3–6 cm long and finely dentate. Slightly pubescent beneath when young and bright emerald in colour. Autumn tints yellow to reddish-brown.

Flowers: February–April, usually before leaves. Bisexual, entomophilous. Pure

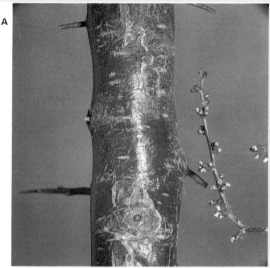

white and prolific, about 12–19 mm across, singly or 2 together on a short, glabrous stalk, each having 5 petals and 15–20 stamens.

Fruit: Ripen September–October. A globose fleshy drupe about 12 mm in diameter, erect on a short stalk, bluish-black with a whitish bloom. The astringent greenish flesh encloses a hard stone. Fruit yield heaviest on trees in soils of high pH.

A Bark, Blackthorn. **B** Flowers, Blackthorn.
C Berries, Blackthorn.

Magnoliaceae
Tulip Tree—*Liriodendron tulipifera* L.

Tulip Tree

Description
This elegant, fast-growing, deciduous tree can reach a height of 60 m in its native America, but in Europe it is usually only half that height. It is straight- and single-stemmed with many short, tortuous branches which are pendant at the extremities, giving a columnar outline with a rounded dome. It has a life-span of over 300 years.

Timber
White to olive green, occasionally with purplish-green streaks. Soft, light, straight grained with very fine, even texture, and taking a good polish. Neither strong nor durable, yet a useful timber when available, and easy to work. Uses include flooring, furniture, carving, engineers patterns and dairy utensils. In Britain the timber is referred to as 'canary wood' or 'American whitewood'.

Range and Habitat
Not indigenous in Europe. Native to eastern N. America and one of the largest deciduous trees of that area. Introduced to Britain in the latter half of the 17th century; some of the original trees are still standing. Frequently seen as an ornamental tree in parks and large gardens throughout the milder parts of Europe. It prefers sheltered but sunny situations and deep, loamy soil.

Related Trees
The Chinese Tulip Tree, *Liriodendron chinense* (Hemsl.) Sarg., is closely related to *L. tulipifera* but is usually of shorter stature, has smaller flowers and deeper, more acutely angled leaf lobes. Introduced from China and rare as an ornamental in Europe. Tulip trees are in the same family as the magnolias, of which there are some 35 species, represented only in N. and Central America and eastern Asia.

Associated Macro-fungi
None specific in Britain and Europe.

Associated Insects
None specific in Britain and Europe.

General Information
Known as the Saddle Tree by virtue of the shape of the leaves. Also called Yellow Poplar in America, probably because the leaves flutter Aspen-like in the wind. An extract from the bark is used as a heart stimulant. The Tulip Tree is recommended only for large gardens which are not subject to late frosts.

Bark: Young trees grey then scaly, ageing to brown with an orange tinge, shallowly and evenly furrowed.

Twigs: Brown to reddish-brown, smooth and shiny with prominent stipule scars. Buds reddish-brown, shiny, obovoid, laterally compressed and enclosed in a pair of large stipules.

Leaves: Unfold April–May. Alternate, simple, glabrous, and 4-lobed, up to 13 cm long or broad; terminal lobes shaped in a manner that causes the leaf to appear as if cut off at the apex. Shiny green above, lighter beneath. Petiole very long, slender and angled, causing the leaves to flutter in the lightest of winds. Remain on tree until November, display brilliant golden tints.

Flowers: June–July. Very fragrant, solitary and terminal amongst the leaves. Cup-shaped at first, 5–7.5 cm across, and 5 cm high, with 6 petals in 2 series, each pale green with a broad orange band at the base, and 3 reflexed greenish-white sepals. Inside the flower there are many substantial, long, whitish-coloured stamens surrounding a central cone. By degrees the flower opens wide, the sepals fall and the stamens spread. Blossoms freely only in long warm summers.

Fruit: Ripen dark brown in September. A slender cone-like aggregate of dry fruits which does not open; each fruit carrying 1–2 winged seeds. The

aggregate persists on the tree throughout winter, finally breaking up to release the seeds, which are wind dispersed.

A Bark, Tulip Tree. B Flower, Tulip Tree.
C Unripe fruit, Tulip Tree.

Leguminosae
Common Laburnum or Golden Rain—*Laburnum anagyroides* Medicus

Common
Laburnum

Description
This small, deciduous tree with its light, ascending, arching branches, is very attractive in all aspects, but especially so when in flower. It is erect, rapid-growing and hardy, up to 9 m high, and although some authorities quote it as very short-lived, others disagree; 200 years is probably the maximum life-span in Britain.

Timber
Sapwood yellow, heartwood much darker, coarse grained, very hard, takes a good polish. It is a very durable timber, sometimes called 'false ebony' and similar in appearance to that of False Acacia. Used in cabinet-work, turnery, wood sculpture and woodwind instruments. Veneers of the end grain, known as 'oyster shell' can be used as inlay for furniture.

Range and Habitat
Native to central and southern Europe and found in the wild state mainly in mountainous regions. Introduced to most other parts of Europe (including Britain) over 400 years ago and naturalised in some areas. Grows in most soil types and is tolerant of salty and polluted atmospheres.

Related Trees
The Scottish Laburnum, *L. alpinum* Bercht & Presl, an introduced tree from southern Europe and not native to Scotland, differs from Common Laburnum in being much less hairy on the twigs and leaflets and bearing denser, longer racemes. It also flowers some three weeks later, the pods are hairless with upper suture winged and the seeds ripen brown. The hybrid between Common and Scottish Laburnums, *L.* x *watereri*, is now most popular, having outstanding blossom but sparse fruit. Weeping and upright forms of Common Laburnum are

available. Adams Laburnum, *Laburnocytisus adamii* (Poit.) Schneid., sometimes seen in parks and gardens and on roadsides, is a graft hybrid between *L. anagyroides* and the Purple Broom, *Cytisus purpureus* Scop. This small tree or shrub bears racemes of yellow laburnum flowers, and similar racemes of purple flowers and intermediate coloured flowers on the same tree. It is propagated only from cuttings and originated largely by chance in the nursery of M. D. Adam at Vitry near Paris in 1825.

Associated Macro-fungi
None specific.

Associated Insects
Lepidoptera—Moths: *Leucoptera laburnella* Staint., larvae mine leaves making a spiral blotch. **Diptera**—True flies: *Agromyza demeijerei* Hendel, larvae mine leaves making a narrow linear mine near leaf margin, later making a blotch mine. *Phytomyza cytisi* Brischke, larvae mine leaves making a whitish, linear, irregular mine.

General Information
Gerard, in his *Herbal* published in 1597, stated that a laburnum grew in his garden; presumably it must have been well established in Britain at that date. All parts of all laburnums are poisonous to humans, but allowing for this, they make excellent garden or park trees.

Bark: Smooth, greyish-green to brownish-green. Poisonous to cattle, although rabbits eating the bark are unaffected.

Twigs: Greyish-green to olive, smooth with silky-grey adpressed hairs. Buds alternate, ovoid with few scales, pale grey and hairy.

Leaves: Unfold May. Compound; leaflets 3, ovate-lanceolate, 3–8 cm long, margins entire. Dark greyish-green, pubescent beneath. Petioles 5–7.5 cm; stipules small. Autumn tint yellow.

Flowers: Late May–early June. Bisexual, entomophilous. Bright yellow, papilionaceous, 2 cm long, crowded in pendulous, terminal, pubescent racemes each 10–30 cm long. Usually profuse on the tree but short-lived and soon fade.

Fruit: A 1-celled, hard, downy, green pod becoming black, 5–7.5 cm long with upper edge thickened and keeled, but not winged, hanging in bunches. Seeds 2–7, black when ripe, kidney-shaped. Very poisonous, sometimes fatal to human beings.

A Bark, Common Laburnum.
B Flower, Common Laburnum.
C Developing seed pods, Common Laburnum.

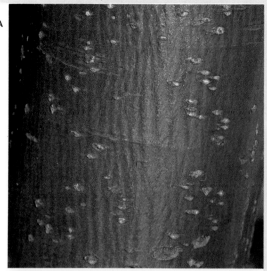

Leguminosae
Gorse, Furze or Whin—*Ulex europaeus* L.

Gorse

Description
Gorse is a dense, evergreen shrub with copious branched spines and few leaves. It usually grows to a height of 0.5–1.5 m but will occasionally reach 3.5 m in sheltered places. It is at first erect and compact, but later spreads untidily, the lower foliage becoming brown and long persisting.

Timber
Creamy-white, fairly heavy, coarse grained and fibrous with many blackish knot-marks right to the core. Unsubstantial and of no commercial consequence. Burns cheerfully even when green.

Range and Habitat
Native to western and central Europe, but not a Mediterranean species. Very frequent on heaths, commons, motorway embankments and wasteland. Common in the British Isles, less so in northern Scotland. Prefers light acid substrates; tolerant of sea winds and air pollution.

Related Trees
Western Gorse, *U. gallii* Planch., native to western England, E. Anglia, Wales, S.W. Scotland, Ireland and parts of western Europe, is smaller than *U. europaeus* and flowers only from August to November. The spines are only lightly furrowed; the bracts on the flower stalk narrow and minute. Dwarf Gorse, *U. minor* Roth., found in S.E. England, is a very small, more prostrate shrub with weak spines which flowers from July to September.

Associated Macro-fungi
Lignicolous—*Polyporus lentus* Berk., a small, stipitate bracket species found on dead stems and roots. *Flammulina velutipes* (Fries) Karst., Winter Fungus, grows in tufts August–April on living or dead branches. (Neither are confined to Gorse.)

Associated Insects
Lepidoptera—Moths: *Scopopteryx mucronata mucronata* Scop., Common Lead Belle; *S. luridata plumbaria* F., July Lead Belle, larvae feed on foliage. *Onocera genistella* Dupon., larvae gregarious in web. *Cydia internana* Guenée, larvae feed in seeds. *Mirificarma mulinella* Zell.; *Brachmia gerronella* Zell., larvae feed in flowers. *Batia lambdella* Donov., larvae in dead twigs. *Agonopterix ulicetella* Staint., larvae in spun shoots. *Scythris grandipennis* Haworth, larvae in web on shoot. *Coleophora albicosta* Haworth, larvae in seeds. *Phyllonorycter ulicicolella* Staint., larvae in bark. **Coleoptera**—Weevils: *Apion ulicis* Foerst.; *A. scutellare* Kirby, cause swellings on shoots (mainly on Dwarf Gorse). *Sitona regensteinensis* Herbst.; *Polydrusus confluens* Steph. Bark beetles: *Phloeophthorus rhododactylus* Marsh.; *Hylastinus obscurus* Marsh. **Homoptera**—Leaf-hopper: *Livilla ulicis* Curt.

General Information
The word furze is derived from the Anglo-Saxon name for Gorse, 'Fyrs'. It used to be grown extensively for use as cattle or horse fodder. The foliage was cut and then crushed or pulped and the yield was generally about 18 tons per acre (45 tonnes per hectare) every three years. The long length of the flowering season has given rise to the saying 'When Gorse is out of flower, kissing is out of season.' Gorse makes valuable game cover and is excellent for wildlife but is a considerable fire hazard. In cultivation it is best grown from seed in the intended situation, or sown in pots to be planted out later with minimum disturbance to the root system.

Bark: Thin, dark brown, rough and fibrous, flakes off in vertical strips.

Twigs: None as such, new growth developing into deeply furrowed, dark green, minutely pubescent, fairly

straight spines which in turn bear more spines or spiny leaves.

Leaves. Sparse. Seedling leaves compound with 3 leaflets. Adult leaves spiny or reduced to scales. Exstipulate.

Flowers: At any time of the year but mainly February–May and August–September. Bisexual, entomophilous. Canary-yellow, fragrant, borne abundantly. Each flower solitary on a short stalk in the axils of the previous year's spines, pea-like 18 mm long, stamens 10, monadelphous. Calyx yellow like the petals but slightly shorter and densely clothed in brownish hairs, as are also the 2 small cordate bracts at the base.

Fruit: A legume or 1 -celled downy green pod, oval-oblong about 2 cm long, containing a few green seeds. When ripe the pod becomes blackish and rough with brown hairs. It explodes with an audible crack, the dark seeds being thrown some distance away, from whence many are dispersed by insects. They do not readily germinate, often only springing into life years later after being scorched by fire.

A Habit, Gorse. **B** Flower, Gorse.
C Seed pods, Gorse.

Leguminosae   Subfamily Lotoideae
False Acacia or Locust Tree—*Robinia pseudoacacia* L.

False Acacia

Description
When open grown and mature, this deciduous tree is airy and stately with tortuous, brittle and spidery branches, a broad, open crown and scanty foliage. The bole is usually short, soon dividing into two or more lengthy branches. A long-lived and tenacious tree, the False Acacia grows rapidly in its early years to heights of 12–24 m, with proportionate girths up to 5.5 m. It is freely suckering and if felled, quickly commences new growth.

Timber
Hard, strong, durable and fine grained but liable to split or crack. At one time its virtues were manifestly extolled, but experience proved that timber grown in Britain had limited usage. The pins or trenails used to fasten the planks to a ship's ribs were often made of False Acacia. Burns well.

Range and Habitat
Native to eastern and mid-western N. America; introduced to Europe in 1601. Grows best in light, neutral or slightly acid substrates; tolerant of air pollution.

Related Trees
Varieties include 'Decaisneana' which bears pale pink flowers, 'Frisia' with golden leaves, 'Fastigiata' with an upright and very narrow form and 'Pendula' with a weeping habit.

Associated Macro-fungi
None specific in Britain and Europe.

Associated Insects
Hymenoptera—North American sawfly: *Pteronidea trilineata* Norton has been recorded in Germany, an importation which does not seem to have established itself.

General Information
Early settlers in America confused this tree with the Locust Bean of the Bible lands, the fruits of which gave sustenance to John the Baptist in the wilderness. The seeds are, in fact, unpalatable, but the roots afford an extract similar to liquorice. The genus is named after Jean Robin, herbalist to Henry IV of France and Professor of Botany at the Jardin des Plantes, Paris, who received the first seeds to come to Europe in 1601. The species enjoyed a brief period of popularity but was then forgotten until about 1820, when William Cobbett started importing saplings from the USA, proclaiming that the timber would become more popular than oak. Although there was an immediate response and Cobbett sold over a million trees, the popularity was short-lived. The False Acacia is not recommended for the small garden. If exposed to strong winds, larger trees show a tendency to lose branches suddenly, nevertheless the species is often planted as a roadside tree, is useful as a soil improver and helps prevent erosion on waste tips etc.

Bark: Brown and smooth in young trees; later greyish-brown and rough with long deep ridges both broad and narrow, often arranged in a beautiful interlaced pattern.

Twigs: Olive brown, very brittle and armed with short, paired spines. Buds minute, naked and set alternately.

Leaves: Unfold late May. Compound-pinnate, 15–20 cm long, leaflets 7–19 including terminal, 3–5 cm long, elliptic or ovate, margin entire, sometimes with apex notched or shortly spined. Glabrous, bright green above, glaucous or bluish-green beneath. Petiole short; stipules spiny. Autumn tint yellow.

Flowers: June. Bisexual, entomophilous. White, fragrant, papilionaceous and numerous, borne in a pendulous

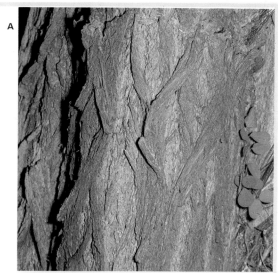

raceme 10–20 cm long. Petals 5,
stamens 9, united, 1 free.

Fruit: A thin 1-celled pod which
persists throughout winter, 5–10 cm
long, dark brown and glabrous,
containing 4–8 seeds which are brown,
streaked with black.

A Bark, False Acacia.
B Flowers and leaves, False Acacia.
C Seed pods, False Acacia.

Aceraceae
Common or Field Maple—*Acer campestre* L.

Description
The Common Maple is a deciduous tree up to 10 m high, but occasionally double this height, with light, upswept, spreading branches. However, it is more often seen as a straggly shrub in thickets or hedgerows.

Timber
Pale brown, soft, fine grained and beautifully veined, especially the wood from the roots. Not substantial enough for structural purposes, yet ideal for turnery or carving and takes a high polish. Makes excellent fuel.

Range and Habitat
Native to Europe apart from the far North. The tree can be found as an introduction in many parts of the British Isles but is indigenous only in calcareous soils of England and Wales and is locally common. It will thrive in all but the most acid substrates, preferring, however, well-drained loamy soils in sheltered locations; tolerates shade from larger trees and resists air pollution.

Related Trees
The Norway Maple, *A. platanoides* L., is a handsome, hardy, vigorous, deciduous tree with broad, rounded head and dense foliage. The maximum height is 28 m with trunk diameters up to 1 m. Generally not long-lived but isolated trees can live for over 200 years. On young trees the bark is smooth and grey, in later life it develops shallow ridges arranged in a network pattern and becomes darker in colour. The twigs are glabrous, terminal winter buds are reddish-brown, the laterals green. The palmate leaves appear April–May and are considerably larger than those of the Field Maple, usually with 5 angular lobes, 3 of which are distinctly pointed at the apex and shoulders; bright green and glabrous above, paler beneath. The fairly long petiole yields white latex when broken. Autumn tints yellow to

Common
Maple

Norway
Maple

reddish. Flowers appear in late March before the leaves, they are greenish-yellow borne in an erect corymbose pannicle of cymes. The fruit is a paired samara, larger than that of Field Maple, the wings are slightly curved and set almost horizontally. The timber is white, greying with age, fine textured and hard; in use it is similar to Sycamore but somewhat inferior. Native to continental Europe, introduced to Britain in the 17th century. It makes a useful ornamental tree and will thrive in most soils and situations. The various Japanese cultivars of *A. palmatum* Thunb. and *A. japonicum* Thunb. make excellent decorative garden trees.

Associated Macro-fungi
None known to be specific.

Associated Insects
Lepidoptera—Moths: *Ptilophora plumigera* Denis & Schiff., Plumed Prominent; *Lophopteryx cucullina* Denis, Maple Prominent; *Eupithecia inturbata* Hübn., Maple Pug; *Croesia forsskaleana* L.; *Teleiodes scriptella* Hübn., larvae in folded leaves. *Pammene trauniana* Denis & Schiff.; *Etainia sericopeza* Zell.; *E. sphendamni* Hering, larvae in seeds. *Phyllonorycter sylvella* Haworth, larvae in mine on underside of leaves. *Caloptilia semifascia* Haworth; *Calybites pyrenaeella* Chretien, larvae in rolled leaves. *Ypsolopha sequella* Clerck, larvae in slight web on leaves.
Homoptera—Aphids: *Drepanosiphum aceris* Koch; *Periphyllus hirticornis* Walker; *P. testudinaceus* Fern. Leaf-hoppers: *Rhinocola aceris* L.
Hymenoptera—Sawflies: *Heterarthrus aceris* Kaltenb.; *Pristiphora subbifida* Thomson, larvae on leaves. **Diptera**—Gall midges: *Dasyneura acercrispans* Kief.; *Atrichosema aceris* Kief.

General Information
In the past, children were passed through the branches of this tree in

order that they might gain longevity. The name Maple is derived from 'mapwl', a Celtic word. In parts of France the tough shoots were used as horse whips. Many of the smaller maples are suitable for the garden and for public places, where their foliage will provide excellent autumn colouring.

Bark: Variable, grey to brown or pinkish-brown, smooth or fissured with corky ribs.

Twigs: Light brown and pubescent, sometimes roughened and bearing longitudinal, straight, continuous, corky ribs, occurring even on the shoots of the year. Buds 5 mm long, brown, narrowly ovate and ciliate.

Leaves: Unfold April–May. Opposite, ivy-like and very variable in outline and size, 4–7.5 cm long and slightly broader than long, bluntly 5-lobed; margin usually entire, but some trees have leaves with indented edges. Initially pinkish, then light green, becoming darker; underside duller, pubescent at first, veins remain pubescent. Petiole long and slender, green or reddish, exudes milky juice when broken; exstipulate. Autumn tints yellow, red or golden brown.

Flowers: April–May. Greenish, 6 mm in diameter, 10 or more in erect branching clusters, Anemophilous or entomophilous, lower flowers staminate, upper bisexual, sometimes protandrous. Petals 5, sepals 5, sepals broader than petals.

Fruit: A paired samara in bunches of 2–4, each wing about 4 cm long, the two wings aligned horizontally or nearly so. Green then purplish-red, finally brown. Dispersed by wind. Seed vessels minutely pubescent, wings glabrous.

A Bark, Common Maple.
B Leaves and flowers, Common Maple.
C Leaves and fruit, Norway Maple.

Aceraceae
Sycamore or Great Maple—*Acer pseudoplatanus* L.

Sycamore

Description
A fast-growing, deciduous tree, the Sycamore is usually handsome in outline when open grown. When mature it is 12–30 m high with a broadly-rounded crown and large, ascending, rounded branches, emanating from a substantial bole with buttressed base. The raft-like foliage is abundant, becoming thick and heavy by high summer. It has a life-span of 150–250 years but may survive for up to 500 years.

Timber
Young wood soft and whitish, old wood creamy, fine grained, hard, smooth and shiny. There is a reasonable demand and many uses, which include turnery, furniture, domestic and agricultural utensils, rollers, and parts of string instruments. Makes good firewood.

Range and Habitat
Native to south and central Europe; introduced to Britain in the Middle Ages, probably as an ornamental tree. Common today in most parts of Britain and completely naturalised, sometimes becoming a nuisance, for its many seeds disperse widely and germinate readily. Thrives best on fertile soil but will grow well in any substrate that is not too wet, even in the millstone grit areas of the Pennines; the trees planted more than a century ago stand straight and shapely around the ruins of long-abandoned farmsteads, outstanding proof of real hardiness! Windfirm and tolerant of air pollution or sea spray.

Related Trees
The varieties *A. pseudoplatanus* var. *purpureum*, with purple undersides to its leaves, and *A. pseudoplatanus* var. *variegatum*, with pale green leaves blotched with white, are often planted in public places.

Associated Macro-fungi
Lignicolous—*Polyporus squamosus* Fries, Dryad's Saddle, a wound parasite. *Nectria cinnabarina* Fries, Coral Spot, on newly felled branches.

Associated Insects
Lepidoptera—Moths: *Ptilophora plumigera* Denis & Schiff.; *Acronicta aceris* L., Sycamore Moth, larvae feed on leaves. *Croesia forsskaleana* L., larvae in folded leaves. *Pammene regiana* Zell., larvae in seeds. *Phyllonorycter geniculella* Rago.; *Caloptilia hemidactylella* Denis & Schiff.; *Nepticula speciosa* Frey; *Etainia decentella* Herr.-Schaeff., larvae mine leaves. **Homoptera**—Aphids: *Drepanosiphum acerinum* Walker; *D. platanoides* Schrank; *Periphyllus acericola* Walker; *P. testudinaceus* Fern. (the most abundant British species). **Hymenoptera**—Sawflies: *Pristiphora subbifida* Thomson; *Heterarthrus aceris* Kaltenb. **Diptera**—True flies: *Contarinia acerplicans* Kief., small gall on leaves. *Dasyneura acercrispans* Kief., leaves reddened and veins thickened.

General Information
The true Sycamore is an eastern tree, *Ficus sycomorus* L. (Fig-mulberry), but due to some confusion by early European botanists, the name has been wrongly applied to *A. pseudoplatanus*. In Scotland, the tree is often referred to as 'Plane', another misnomer. In common with many other maples the sap carries a high sugar content which, when the tree is infested with aphids, makes the leaves very sticky. This makes it an unsuitable tree for urban and industrial areas as the leaves inevitably accumulate grime. The heavy fall of leaves in autumn and the readily-germinating seeds also pose problems for gardens and parks. Virtually useless for wildlife. The black spots often seen on the leaves are caused by a micro-fungus, *Rhytisma acerinum* (St Amans) Fries, Tar spot or Maple Blotch. The presence of this disease is said to indicate a clean atmosphere.

Bark: At first dark grey and smooth; after 30 years or so becoming brownish-grey and broken up into rough, irregular shapes which lift at the extremities and are apt to flake off showing a pinkish-brown coloration beneath.

Twigs: Pale brown, stout and glabrous. Winter buds ovoid-pointed, up to 13 mm long, set in pairs; scales olive green with brown border.

Leaves: Unfold April or May. Opposite, palmately 5-lobed and unequally serrate. Leaf-size can vary considerably from 10 to 20 cm long, as can the depths of lobes. Petiole long and slender, green-yellow or red, not exuding milky juice when broken; exstipulate. Autumn tints yellow to brown.

Flowers: April–June. Staminate or bisexual, entomophilous, protandrous. Greenish-yellow, 60–100 in pendulous clusters up to 14 cm long on outside of tree.

Fruit: Produced after 20 years. A samara, scimitar-shaped and paired, wings divergent at right-angles. Reddish-green, then brown before the fall in October.

A Bark, Sycamore. **B** Flowers, Sycamore.
C Fruit and leaves, Sycamore.

A

B

C

Hippocastanaceae
White or Common Horse Chestnut — *Aesculus hippocastanum* L.

White Horse
Chestnut

Description
The White Horse Chestnut is one of the most attractive of trees in all seasons and at all stages, especially when growing in open parkland or in avenues. In sheltered areas it grows vigorously, straight and true, and when mature is up to 40 m high with a huge, domed crown and massive lower branches which sweep gently upwards, level out and then curve downwards. The bole is short, stout, cylindrical and buttressed, often developing a slight twist, with a girth of up to 6 m. 150 years is a good age for the species, but some trees may double this life-span.

Timber
Creamy-white, very soft, non-durable and close grained. Of little commercial value and makes poor fuel.

Range and Habitat
Native to the Balkan Peninsula; introduced to Britain in the 16th century. It is not conservative in its soil requiremenťs, but thrives best in fertile areas which are not exposed to strong winds. Tolerant of air pollution.

Related Trees
There are some 25 species of *Aesculus*, most of which occur in N. America, with a few in southern Europe, the Himalayas, China and Japan. The Red Horse Chestnut, *A.* x *carnea* Hayne, often seen in Britain and in Europe, is a hybrid between *A. hippocastanum* and the American species, *A. pavia* L. Its flowers are red, the fruits are small and not very prickly, and the winter buds are not sticky. Lacking vigour, it is prone to disease and is consequently short-lived.

Associated Macro-fungi
None specific in Britain.

Associated Insects
Very few. **Lepidoptera** — Micro-moths: *Cnephasia incertana* Treit., larvae mine leaves. *C. stephensiana* Doubl., polyphagous, usually on very young trees. *Argyresthia glaucinella* Zell., larvae in bark.

General Information
The fruits, known as conkers, contain tannins and saponins, and it is said that they were fed to broken-winded horses in Asia Minor, this being a possible explanation for the tree's common name. The decayed conkers become jelly-like and have been used as washing soap. Although possessing fine qualities, it requires too much space for the average garden.

Bark: Greyish-brown to purplish-brown, smooth at first, becoming rough and irregularly scaly; the scales flake off as the tree ages.

Twigs: Thick and robust, reddish-brown with pale lenticels. Winter buds noticeably large, brown, scaly, resinous and sticky; apart from the terminal, set in opposite pairs. Leaf-scars clearly horseshoe-shaped.

Leaves: Unfold late March or early April. Palmate, with 5–7 obovate leaflets, each 10–25 cm long with double dentate edges, all on a single stalk up to 20 cm long. Pale green and pubescent ᴊt first, soon becoming glabrous and darker. Autumn tints variable hues of reds, yellows and browns.

Flowers: April–May. Bisexual, entomophilous. On an erect stalk, each bearing 10–20 5-petalled blooms with 5–8 stamens. Petals white marked with pink and yellow.

Fruit: The involucre is a thick green globose outer covering about 6 cm in diameter carrying substantial brownish

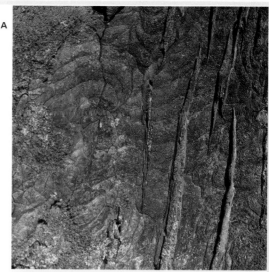

spikes, contrasting with the white, down-lined cells within. Each involucre may hold 1–3 round or flat-sided shiny brown nuts (conkers), each with a large round white mark, which soon darkens after release. They are eaten by certain animals, but are bitter tasting and not recommended for human consumption.

A Bark, White Horse Chestnut.
B Flowers, White Horse Chestnut.
C Fruit, White Horse Chestnut.

Aquifoliaceae
Holly—*Ilex aquifolium* L.

Holly

Description
Holly is a very long-lived, slow-growing and comparatively small, evergreen tree, with dense, dark, shiny foliage. It normally grows to 3–12 m in height but is occasionally taller: a specimen in Surrey, England was said to be 24 m high. The girth is variable in mature trees and although usually 1–2 m, it can be double this. Growing normally, the tree has a single main stem, with or without light branches down to the base, and is pyramidal or spire-shaped.

Timber
White or off-white, even grained, hard and heavy. In demand for turnery and marquetry, e.g. printing blocks, chessmen and whip handles etc.; a substitute for boxwood or ebony if dyed black. Burns readily, as does the foliage, even when newly felled.

Range and Habitat
Native throughout western, central and southern Europe. In the British Isles, excluding the far north, it is a common tree, but more so in the west than in the east. It cannot survive arctic conditions for any length of time. It is not conservative in its choice of habitat but thrives best in soils with high humus content; once established it should not be transplanted. Tolerant of air pollution and briny winds.

Related Trees
Representatives of the family are found in both the northern and southern hemispheres and there are over 300 species. A common species of N. America is *I. opaca* Aiton, with lighter coloured foliage than *I. aquifolium* and lacking the glossy sheen. There are also many well-known cultivars.

Associated Macro-fungi
Marasmius hudsonii (Fries) Fries, may be found on dead leaves beneath the trees.

Associated Insects
Lepidoptera—Butterfly: *Celastrina argiolus* L., Holly Blue, first brood eggs laid on flower buds. Tortrix moth: *Rhopobota unipunctana* Haworth (*naevana* Hübn.), larvae feed on leaves. **Homoptera**—Aphid: *Aphis ilicis* Kaltenb., infestations cause leaf distortion. **Diptera**—*Phytomyza ilicis* Curt., larvae commonly mine leaf blades.

General Information
Holly is associated with many superstitions and religious observances, and it used to be planted near homesteads to ward off lightning and keep away witches. It makes an ideal sound-proof, animal-proof hedge. In parts of Europe the leaves are used to make a kind of tea. It is also known as Helver, Holm, Hollin, Aunt Mary's Tree and Poisonberry.

Bark: Grey with a silvery quality, fine and delicate, smooth or finely fissured in old trees, often bearing large protuberances. Used in the manufacture of bird-lime.

Twigs: Glabrous, green or purplish. Buds minute.

Leaves: Evergreen. Alternate, simple, ovate and thick, margin undulate and spiny on lower part of tree. Dark glossy green above, paler below and glabrous. Petiole short.

Flowers: Early May–June. Normally dioecious, entomophilous. Each 6–8 mm across, in small axillary clusters, waxy-white and fragrant with 4 petals and 4 stamens; the male with a functionless ovary, the female bearing a 4-celled ovary.

Fruit: Ripen July onwards, on female trees only. Berries 7–10 mm in diameter, green at first, ripening to red through the autumn and persisting into the spring unless taken by birds. They are poisonous to human beings. The shed

seed does not germinate until the
following year or the year after that.

A Bark, Holly. B Flowers, Holly.
C Leaves and berries, Holly.

Celastraceae
Spindle Tree—*Euonymus europaeus* L.

Spindle Tree

Description
The Spindle Tree is a straggling, though pretty, deciduous shrub or small tree which may occasionally grow to 8 m in height and which sometimes lives to 100 years.

Timber
White, very hard and smooth grained. Before the advent of the spinning jenny the wood was used extensively for making spindles. Other uses include knitting needles, toothpicks, skewers, small turnery and drawing charcoal.

Range and Habitat
Native on suitable substrates in scrub and hedgerows throughout most of temperate Europe including the British Isles; but in Scotland only found in the southern part. Prefers base-rich substrates but will thrive in slightly acid soils where planted.

Related Trees
The Broad-leaved Spindle Tree, *E. latifolius* Scop., is a similar tree and native of central and S.E. Europe but introduced to the British Isles in 1863. It bears white flowers which fade to purple, has larger leaves and berries and is more vigorous than *E. europaeus*. The Japanese Spindle Tree, *E. japonicus* L., with dark green shiny leaves, is another introduced species tolerant of sea salt and air pollution, but unattractive when planted for hedging.

Associated Macro-fungi
Lignicolous—*Phellinus ribis* (Schum. ex Fries) Karst., a small, thin and brightly coloured bracket fungus.

Associated Insects
Lepidoptera—Moths: *Ligdia adustata* Denis & Schiff., Scorched Carpet, larvae on leaves. *Alispa angustella* Hübn., larvae in berries. *Yponomeuta plumbella* Denis & Schiff., larvae at first in shoots, later in spun webs. *Y. irorella* Hübn.; *Y. cagnagella* Hübn., larvae in slight web. **Homoptera**—Aphid: *Aphis fabae* Scop., 'Black Fly', overwinters as egg on Spindle, in summer attacks Broad Beans. **Diptera**—True flies: *Liriomyza strigata* Meigen, larvae mine leaves.

General Information
The powdered fruit is considered a powerful insecticide and the boiled fruit has been used as a hair rinse. Red dye is obtained from the husk and yellow dye from the pulp. All parts of the tree when crushed or bruised give off a fetid odour. Being hardy and remarkably beautiful in autumn, the Spindle is suitable for most gardens.

Bark: Smooth and grey, lightly fissured with age.

Twigs: Opposite, square or round, straight, smooth and distinctly dark green. Buds generally opposite, short, slightly square-sided and green.

Leaves: Unfold April–May. Oblong-lanceolate or ovate, 3–12.5 cm long, shallowly serrate. Glabrous, bluish-green below. Stipules small. Autumn tints very beautiful in crimson, purple and gold.

Flowers: May–June. Bisexual, staminate or pistillate, entomophilous. On long-stalked cymes from the leaf axils. Each flower about 1 cm across, greenish-white, usually with 4 petals, 4 sepals and a short, protruding pistil.

Fruit: A flattened, 4-lobed, 4-celled aril about 12 mm across, green then pale pink, finally deep rosy-pink by September–October. The lobes split revealing the black seeds, which at first are covered in an orange pulp. They are eaten and distributed by birds, but are emetic and poisonous to humans.

A Bark, Spindle Tree.
B Flowers and leaves, Spindle Tree.
C Berries, Spindle Tree.

A

B

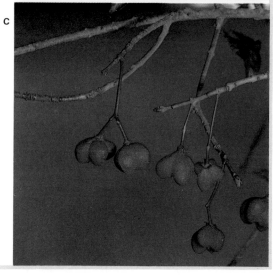

C

Buxaceae
Common Box—*Buxus sempervirens* L.

Common Box

Description
The Common Box is a very slow-growing, long-living bush or small tree of narrow habit up to 6 m high with a maximum girth of 60 cm. The branches are light, downy when young, erect or downswept and densely foliated, especially at the crown. The tree-form described is rare, and confined to a few areas ideally suited to its growth.

Timber
Yellow, very fine grained, very hard and so dense that it does not float on water; takes a high polish. In demand for engraving, carving and small tools but not used as much today as formerly.

Range and Habitat
Native to southern Europe, N. Africa and western Asia, where it is locally common. In the British Isles only found in the natural state in a very few localities in southern England, including the famous Box Hill site in Surrey. Dry chalk hills and limestone areas are its chosen haunt, but thrives on most soils when planted; as it so often is in parks and gardens throughout Britain and Europe. Like the Yew it makes an excellent hedge and is held in high esteem for topiary work. Not tolerant of air pollution.

Related Trees
The species of the Buxaceae family are mainly tropical. There are several cultivars of the Common Box but the only other species likely to be found in British parks and gardens is the Balearic Box, *B. balearica* Lam. This is indigenous to the Balearic Isles, Sardinia and southern Spain, and bears larger leaves and flower clusters than Common Box.

Associated Macro-fungi
Marasmius buxi Fries, on fallen leaves.

Associated Insects
Homoptera—Leaf-hoppers: *Psylla buxi*
L., causes shoot distortion. **Diptera**—Gall midge: *Monarthropalus buxi* Laboul., causes swellings on leaf especially near midrib.

General Information
The herbalist had many uses for Box bark, leaves and seeds. A decoction made from the leaves was believed to prevent premature baldness, but, apart from purging and raising the body temperature, probably little benefit was derived from its use. In respect for the deceased at funerals, sprigs and wreaths of Box were often carried and thrown into the graves by mourners. In 1815 the trees felled on Box Hill fetched around £10,000, a fortune when related to present day money values. John Evelyn, the well known 17th-century horticulturalist and scenic architect, stated 'He that in winter should behold some of our highest hills in Surrey clad with whole woods of these trees [Box and Yew] for divers miles in circuit, might, without the least violence to his imagination fancy himself transported into some new or enchanted country. For if in any spot of England, eternal spring and summer all the year—tis here.' Box is commonly attacked by a micro-fungus, *Puccinia buxi*, Box Leaf Rust (see plate B).

Bark: Pale brown to grey, rough with square cut pattern.

Twigs: More or less 4-angled in section and pubescent; older stems often contorted or twisted. Buds very small, pale orange-brown and pubescent.

Leaves: Evergreen. Sub-opposite, leathery, ovate, 1–2.5 cm long, margin somewhat rounded in and notched at the apex. Shining dark green above, paler green below. Emit a distinctive sweetish odour.

Flowers: April–May. Monoecious, entomophilous. Greenish or yellowish-white, 4 sepals without petals, small and inconspicuous in axillary clusters, usually one female flower with several lateral male flowers each with 4 stamens.

Fruit: Ripen September. A hard, green to brown, 3-valved, ovoid capsule 8 mm long, ending in 3 short diverging beaks, each cell contains 1–2 shiny black seeds.

A Habit, Common Box.
B Flowers and leaves with rust fungus (*Puccinia buxi* DC.), Common Box.
C Leaves and unripe berries, Common Box.

Rhamnaceae
Alder Buckthorn or Berry-bearing Alder—*Frangula alnus* Mill.

Description
The Alder Buckthorn is an erect, deciduous shrub or small tree, up to 4.5 cm high bearing slender, alternate, ascending, purplish-brown branches without thorns and rather scanty foliage.

Timber
Light yellow to yellowish-red, soft and spongy, often referred to as black dogwood. Still used in the manufacture of high-grade gunpowder, but otherwise of no commercial importance.

Range and Habitat
Native throughout most of Europe. In England and Wales it is locally common and may be found in damp woods, thickets and hedges; much preferring acid substrates, especially lowland peat-mosses. Rare in Ireland and absent from Scotland.

Alder Buckthorn

Related Trees
The Mediterranean Buckthorn, *Rhamnus alaternus* L., introduced into Britain in the 17th century, is an evergreen bushy shrub or small tree up to 6 m high, bearing small, green, dioecious, honey-scented flowers in dense clusters. In general appearance it resembles Broad-leaved Jasmine Box, *Phillyrea latifolia* L., although this species has opposite leaves, not alternate as in buckthorns. Purging Buckthorn, *Rhamnus catharticus* L., is a small deciduous tree or shrub of woods, thickets and hedgerows chiefly on calcareous soils. The branchlets are spreading and opposite, the smaller ones often with terminal thorns. The bark is blackish and scaly, the underbark orange coloured. Leaves unfold April, tufted on the shoots, ovate or elliptical and minutely serrate; shortly petiolate and yellowish-green. Flowers appear May–June, very small and yellowish-green, singly or in

Purging Buckthorn

clusters; dioecious and entomophilous. Fruit a globose pea-sized drupe containing 4 seeds. Green at first ripening black in September. They are extremely purgative. Timber is hard, whitish to reddish-yellow and little used commercially. The tree is native and widely distributed throughout temperate Europe, common on the calcareous substrates of Britain apart from Scotland.

Associated Macro-fungi
None specific.

Associated Insects
Lepidoptera—Butterfly: *Gonepteryx rhamni* L., Brimstone, larvae feed openly on leaves. Moths: *Ancylis unculana* Haworth, larvae in spun leaf. *A. obtusana* Haworth, larvae in spun shoot. *Stigmella catharticella* Staint., larvae mine leaves. **Homoptera**—Aphid: *Aphis nasturtii* Kaltenb., causes rolled leaf margins. **Hymenoptera**—Sawfly: *Eriocampa ovata* L., larvae on leaves. **Diptera**—Gall midges: *Contarinia rhamni* Rübs.; *Dasyneura frangulae* Rübs., larvae cause leaf swellings.

General Information
The bark yields a yellow dye and the unripe fruits a green dye. Both bark and berries are emetic. The leaves bear some resemblance to those of Alder, hence the English name.

Bark: Thin and purplish-black, lemon yellow beneath, lenticels pale brown.

Twigs: Green then purplish-brown. Buds hairy, without scales.

Leaves: Unfold April–May. Alternate, obovate or elliptical, margins entire, up to 7 cm long. Deep glossy green and smooth when fully developed, lateral veins parallel and conspicuous. Petiole short. Autumn tints red and yellow.

Flowers: May–June. Bisexual. Very

tiny, greenish-white with 5 petals, sepals and stamens, on stalks situated in leaf axils. Solitary or a few together.

Fruit: A globose, fleshy drupe about 12 mm in diameter containing 2–3 stones. Single or in small clusters; green at first, then red and finally purplish-black by September–October, when they are devoured by passerine birds.

A Flowers and leaves, Alder Buckthorn.
B Berries, Alder Buckthorn.
C Flowers and leaves, Purging Buckthorn.
D Berries, Purging Buckthorn.

Elaeagnaceae
Sea Buckthorn or Sallow Buckthorn—*Hippophae rhamnoides* L.

Sea Buckthorn

Description
The Sea Buckthorn is a thorny, thicket-forming, freely suckering, deciduous shrub or willow-like tree up to 3.5 m high. Handsome in its silvery foliage, it bears subpendulous and slender or short and spiny branches and the female has clusters of orange, berry-like fruits in autumn.

Timber
Unsubstantial and of no commercial value.

Range and Habitat
Native throughout much of Europe including eastern and southern England. Elsewhere in the British Isles fairly common in a naturalised state, especially in coastal areas where it is very tolerant of salt winds and dry sandy substrates. In continental Europe it also inhabits mountainous regions and inland valleys.

Associated Macro-fungi
None specific.

Associated Insects
Lepidoptera—Moths: *Gelechia hippophaella* Schrank, larvae in spun shoots. *Adela croesella* Scop., larvae in flat case on fallen leaves. *Spilonota ocellana* Denis & Schiff., in autumn in silk tube on leaf, in spring in buds. **Homoptera**—Leaf-hoppers: *Psylla hippophaes* Foerst., causes leaf distortion.

General Information
The generic name *Hippophae* is derived from an old Greek word meaning 'prickly spurge'. Sea Buckthorn forms very thorny and virtually impenetrable thickets. Nodules on the roots carry nitrogen-fixing organisms. It makes an attractive garden shrub with its silvery foliage and orange berries, but needs to be controlled as it spreads rapidly by suckering.

Bark: Dark brown and smooth at first; later dull black and rough, with risen narrow intersecting longitudinal strips.

Twigs: Very spiny and covered in rusty-bronze scales or appearing as if sprayed with silvery-white lacquer. Buds rusty brown.

Leaves: Unfold April. Alternate, linear, margins entire, up to 8 cm long after flowering. Dull green above, almost glabrous or covered with scattered silvery stellate scales, underside silvery-grey and scurfy, midrib on young leaves with rusty scales. Petiole short. Autumn tint yellow.

Flowers: March–April, before or with leaves. Dioecious. On erect dwarf shoots, very small, inconspicuous and greenish. Females in crowded clusters; males in small spikes in axils of lowest scale-like bracts, stamens 4.

Fruit: September onward. An orange, berry-like drupe 8 mm in diameter and borne in clusters. They are very acidic, yet devoured by many bird species.

A Leaves, Sea Buckthorn.
B Flowers, Sea Buckthorn.
C Berries, Sea Buckthorn.

Tiliaceae
Common Lime—*Tilia* x *vulgaris* Hayne

Description
A handsome and well-proportioned tree, the Common Lime is the tallest broad-leaved tree in Britain, attaining a height of 45 m in favourable localities, with girths of up to 6.5 m. Typically it is single-stemmed and straight with a compact oval crown, and all the branches ascending, the lower ones becoming decidedly arched downwards. It is a freely suckering tree with the trunk often heavily burred and covered with sprouts which are so thick that they tend to detract from the tree's beauty in winter. It is fast-growing and capable of living for at least 500 years.

Timber
Creamy-white, soft and light. Excellent for carving; other uses include hat-blocks, shoe-lasts, artificial limbs, piano keys, beehive frames; at one time leather was cut on planks of lime. The bast was used to make matting, ropes, shoe tops, and even garments.

Common Lime

Range and Habitat
A natural hybrid between the Small-leaved Lime, *T. cordata*, and the Large-leaved Lime, *T. platyphyllos*. Frequently planted throughout temperate Europe including the British Isles, often in parks and on roadsides. Limes prefer rich, fertile soils, but will thrive on most substrates.

Related Trees
The Small-leaved Lime, *T. cordata* Mill., is native to England and Wales, and planted elsewhere in Britain and Europe. Its leaves, which are usually smaller than those of Common Lime, are glabrous apart from brownish tufts in the vein axils. The fruit is thin-walled and only minutely ribbed, if at all. The Large-leaved Lime, *T. platyphyllos* Scop., is native to one or two limestone areas of England and planted elsewhere in Britain and Europe. Its leaves are usually larger than those of Common Lime, densely pubescent beneath

Small-leaved
Lime

(sometimes both sides) and with whitish tufts in the vein axils. Each cyme is 3-flowered; fruit thick-walled, 3–5, prominently ribbed and densely pubescent. The Caucasian Lime, *T. x euchlora* Koch, being less susceptible to aphid attack and therefore free from honey-dew, is the best lime for roadside planting.

Associated Macro-fungi
Many species may be found on or under limes, but none appear to be specific.

Associated Insects
Lepidoptera—Moths: *Mimas tiliae* L., Lime Hawk; *Tiliacea citrago* L., Orange Sallow, larvae feed openly on leaves. *Glyphipteryx linneella* Clerck, larvae on bark. *Bucculatrix thoracella* Thunb., larvae mine leaves when young, later free feeding. *Stigmella tiliae* Frey, larvae in cases on underside of leaves. **Coleoptera**—Beetle: *Ernoporus tiliae* Panz., in dead branches. **Homoptera**—Aphid: *Eucallipterus tiliae* L. **Hymenoptera**—Sawfles: *Caliroa annulipes* Klug; *Parna tenella* Klug; *Pristiphora ruficornis* Oliv., larvae on leaves.

General Information
Although there are very few British legends surrounding the lime tree, there are many stories from continental Europe. Sugar can be made from the sap, honey from lime is excellent, and an agreeable tea made from an infusion of the flowers was once used to treat chronic epilepsy. Grinling Gibbons, the famous 17th-century wood carver, executed much of his work in lime wood. Because limes will withstand any amount of pruning and pollarding, they are often planted on roadsides. However, they are not ideal for this purpose due to the mess created when the flowers fall and due to the sooty mould which attacks the honey-dew on the foliage and then drops off onto the pavement or vehicles below.

Spraying the trunks with maleic hydrazide will prevent sprouts or suckers. Other names for Lime include Linden, Lini, Teili, Tillet and White Wood.

Bark: Grey and smooth for the first 20 years; later vertically and shallowly fissured. Very fibrous bast.

Twigs: Green or reddish, soon glabrous, slightly zig-zag. Buds alternate, reddish-brown and ovoid.

Leaves: Unfold April–May. Cordate, abruptly short pointed, and often unequal sided, 6–10 cm long, sucker leaves larger. Glabrous apart from whitish tufts in main vein axils, light green and soft at first; then coarser and darker, often infested with red nail galls and covered with honey-dew from aphids. Petiole 2–2.5 cm long; stipulate. Autumn tint yellow, leaves often fall in September.

Flowers: June–July. Bisexual, protandrous, entomophilous. In 4- to 10-flowered, long-stalked, pendulous cymes, fragrant and yellowish-white. Each flower about 8 mm in diameter, with 5 petals, 5 sepals, numerous stamens, conspicuous narrow yellowish-green bract on flower stalk, which is common to all species.

Fruit: A broadly ovoid yellowish, thick-walled nutlet, 8 mm across, which is pubescent and faintly ribbed. In clusters, dispersed by the wind, assisted by the narrow bracteole. Fertility uncertain.

A Bark, Common Lime. **B** Flowers, Common Lime. **C** Fruit and leaves, Common Lime.

Cornaceae
Dogwood or Cornel—*Cornus sanguinea* L.

Dogwood

Description
The Dogwood is normally a freely suckering, thicket-forming, erect, deciduous shrub up to 2.5 m high. However, it is occasionally seen in cultivation as a small, round-headed tree up to 6 m high with a girth of around 60 cm. It is very conspicuous in winter with its slender, red-coloured branches and twigs.

Timber
Very hard, horny and tough, non-splitting. Once used for making goads and dags (a dag is a spiked piece of wood used to drive animals). Other uses, past and present, include arrows, ramrods, mill-cogs, tool handles, tooth picks, and skewers. It burns well and makes good charcoal for gunpowder.

Range and Habitat
Indigenous to much of temperate Europe on alkaline and neutral substrates. In Britain locally common as far north as Cumbria; local in Ireland but does not occur naturally in Scotland. Found in thickets, woods, hedges, also a classic coloniser of uncultivated alkaline wasteland, where if permitted it will take over and shade out lesser plants.

Related Trees
Red Osier Dogwood, *C. sericea* L., with red shoots and branches which often arch over and take root, is a native of N. America. The Red-barked or Tartar Dogwood, *C. alba* L., is similar to Red Osier Dogwood but has erect non-suckering shoots and is native to N.E. Asia and Siberia. Both are planted in gardens to good effect and also found naturalised in suitable areas. The Cornelian Cherry, *C. mas* L., native to alkaline soil areas of central and southern Europe, is commonly seen in British gardens as an introduction. It is a small tree up to 8 m high, with smooth, greyish twigs, and small, bright yellow flowers in clusters which open

in February and March before the ovate-acuminate leaves appear. The ovoid fruits ripen red in August and are esculent.

Associated Macro-fungi
None specific.

Associated Insects
Lepidoptera—Moths: *Antispila pfeifferella* Hübn.; *A. treitschkiella* Fisch V. Ros., larvae in blotch mines on leaves. *Coleophora ahenella* Hein., larvae in cases on leaves. *Spatalistis bifasciana* Hübn., larvae in berries. *Pandemis corylana* F., larvae on foliage. **Hymenoptera**—Sawfly: *Allantus melanarius* Klug, larvae on foliage.

General Information
In parts of Russia a handkerchief soaked in the sap is used as a wishing symbol. The name Dogwood is a corruption of 'dagwood'. The specific name *sanguinea*, meaning bloody, refers to the conspicuous red pigmentation of the tree, and the generic name *Cornus*, meaning horny, refers to the hardness of the wood. There are at least 25 local English names including: Bloody Twig, Catteridge Tree, Houndberry Tree, Prick Wood and Widbin. A lotion made from the bark was said to cure mange in dogs. Because of their striking appearance in the winter months, dogwoods are now regularly planted in parks and gardens.

Bark: Scaly, lightly ridged, greyish on main stem, dark red on lighter branches; fetid odour when bruised.

Twigs: Pubescent, bright red. Winter buds red, very slender, without scales, pubescent.

Leaves: Unfold March. Opposite, broadly ovate tapering to a pointed apex 7.5 cm long, margin entire. Light green and hoary at first; later darker and glabrous. Lateral veins curve distinctly towards the leaf apex. Petiole

short, Autumn tints in attractive reds
and purples.

Flowers: June–July. Bisexual,
entomophilous. Numerous in densely-
flowered, erect, terminal cymes, which
are 4–5 cm across, and without bracts.
Each flower about 1 cm across with 4
dull white, lanceolate petals, and 4
stamens alternating with petals. They
have an unpleasant odour but attract
many winged insects. The flower stalks
and calyx are covered in mealy down.

Fruit: In bunches, green, ripening
purplish-black in September, and bitter
tasting. A globular drupe 6 mm in
diameter, containing a stone with 2
seeds. Eaten by birds and contains an
oil which apparently was used for soap
manufacture and burning in lamps.

A Flowers and leaves, Dogwood.
B Berries, Dogwood.
C Flowers and leaves, Red-barked Dogwood.

Araliaceae
Ivy—*Hedera helix* L.

Ivy

Description
Ivy is a woody, evergreen climber with a main stem up to 25 cm in diameter. When climbing, it adheres to the support by means of adventitious, tufted, root-like growths, situated on the sides of the stems nearest the support. When growing along the ground, however, it throws real roots, which penetrate the soil.

Timber
None as such; the wood is soft and porous and thin slices were once used for filtering liquids. The roots were used as knife sharpeners.

Range and Habitat
Native to most of temperate Europe; common in all parts of the British Isles. It appears to have no preference for any particular type of soil and is found growing in woods, hedgerows, on trees, rocks and buildings.

Related Trees
The Persian Ivy, *H. colchica* Koch, native to the Caucasus and Anatolia and introduced to Britain, bears very large, ovate leaves up to 20 cm long on reddish-brown petioles. *H. canariensis* Coutinho, another introduced species in Britain, is a native of The Azores, Portugal, N.W. Africa and The Canaries. It bears dark green ovate leaves on purplish-red petioles. Ivies were exceedingly popular for house and garden in Victorian times, and are currently enjoying renewed popularity. There are countless cultivars from which to choose.

Associated Macro-fungi
Marasmius epiphylloides (Rea) Sacc. & Trot., grows on dead leaves.

Associated Insects
Lepidoptera—Butterfly: *Celastrina argiolus* L., Holly Blue, second brood larvae on flowers in late summer. Micro-moths: *Eupoecilia ambiguella*

Hübn., larvae on flowers and flower buds etc. *Lozotaenia forsterana* F., larvae between spun leaves. *Clepsis consimilana* Hübn., on leaves.
Coleoptera—Beetle: *Kissophagus hederae* Schmitt, found in dead ivy.
Homoptera—Aphid: *Aphis hederae* Kaltenb., causes leaf-roll.

General Information
Ivy is not parasitic; the only damage that it may do to its supporting tree or wall would be due to the weight of foliage. As with many evergreens, ivy has strong connections with Greek and Roman mythology: warriors adorned their armour with its foliage and poets were awarded crowns of ivy as a token of high esteem. Izaak Walton, in *The Compleat Angler*, claimed that the resin which exudes from wounded woody stems of ivy makes bait more attractive to fish. Animals browsing the foliage in small amounts suffer no ill effects, but it should be noted that the milk from cows and goats that have eaten ivy will be tainted.

Bark: Thin, grey, somewhat wrinkled and minutely rough, with lighter coloured lenticels.

Twigs: Green to purplish-red, hardly tapering and following the contour of the ground, building or tree. Buds green, conical, naked and sessile.

Leaves: Evergreen. Alternate, very variable in size and shape. On lower and climbing stems (juvenile stage) 3- to 5-lobed, angular, borne in one plane. On higher, free stems (adult stage) ovate, undivided, borne spirally around the stem; these are associated with the flowering phase. All leaves thick, dark glossy green above with distinct lighter veins; paler green below. Petiole long; exstipulate. Dying leaves turn brown.

Flowers: October–November. Bisexual, entomophilous. Yellowish-green, in rounded umbels on long stalks and confined, with few exceptions, to the

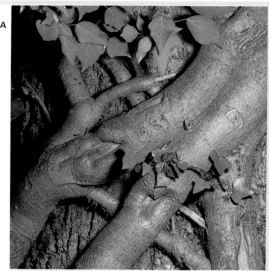

upper branches. Petals 5, broad and short; stamens 5, anthers yellow. Odour unpleasant to humans but very attractive to many insects.

Fruit: Ripen late autumn and winter. A berry-like drupe, diameter 8 mm, green at first then bluish-black with a waxy bloom and green flesh. Seeds 2–5. Unaffected by moderate frost and provide nourishment to many passerine birds at a time when food is scarce.

A Bark (on Common Ash), Ivy.
B Flowers and leaves, Ivy. **C** Berries, Ivy.

Oleaceae
Common Ash—*Fraxinus excelsior* L.

Common Ash

Description
Aptly known as the 'Venus of the woods', the Common Ash has beauty and grace combined with strength. When open grown, the mature tree has an airy, well-proportioned stature, often forked, with ascending branches, the lower ones turning downwards and then upwards again at the extremities. In thick stands it grows tall, slender and straight. In height up to 45 m and with a girth up to 3–6 m, it has a life-span of about 200 years.

Timber
Pale creamy with a tinge of brown, hard, light, strong, very tough, shock-resistant and elastic. The quality varies according to climate and soil fertility. Many uses include small tool handles, shafts and hafts, oars, hockey sticks, carts, wheels, hop-poles and furniture, etc. Makes excellent fuel and charcoal.

Range and Habitat
Native throughout Europe where, when permitted, it readily forms scrub or forest, although it is equally at home in situations such as hedgerows and riversides or on rocky limestone crags. Shallow rooting but windfirm, it prefers a deep, moist, well-drained, base-rich soil, but will subsist on all but the most acid of substrates.

Related Trees
Over 50 species of ash are found in the northern hemisphere. There is a weeping cultivar, 'Pendula', of *F. excelsior* sometimes seen in large, old country gardens, also a rare sport variety, 'Diversifolia', which bears simple oval leaves. The Manna Ash or Flowering Ash, *F. ornus* L., a desirable ornamental introduced into Britain over two centuries ago from southern Europe, is frequently planted in parks, gardens and on roadsides. It has smooth grey bark and bears fragrant, dense, creamy-white flowers in May and the compound leaves are downy beneath. Branches

exude a sweet gum which is used medicinally. The White Ash, *F. americana* L., from eastern N. America and seen occasionally as an alien in Europe, is similar in size to Common Ash. The bark is grey and shortly but deeply fissured, the dioecious flowers appear in May, and the compound leaves are large and usually have 7 long-pointed leaflets.

Associated Macro-fungi
Lignicolous—*Inonotus hispidus* (Bull. ex Fries) Karst.; and *Daldinia concentrica* (Fries) Cesati & de Not., Cramp Ball, fruit bodies on the trunks and branches of sickly trees.

Associated Insects
Lepidoptera—Moths: *Atethmia xerampelina* Esper, Centre-barred Sallow; *Eupithecia innotata* Hufn., Angle-barred Pug; *E. innotata fraxinata* Crewe, Ash Pug (sometimes regarded as a separate species); *Euzophera pinguis* Haworth, in living bark. *Zelleria hepariella* Staint., in silken webs on leaves. *Prays curtisellus* Donov., in mine and later in shoots. **Hymenoptera**—Sawflies: *Tomostethus nigritus* F. **Diptera**—Gall midges: *Dasyneura fraxini* Bremi, pod-like swelling on either side of midrib. *Contarinia marchali* Kief., in fruit.

General Information
The ash used to be the subject of much legend and superstition, and it was also credited with great healing powers. It was said that snakes would never resort even under its 'shadow'. The well known rhyme concerning the appearance of leaves in spring, 'Oak before ash, we're in for a splash; Ash before oak, we're in for a soak,' is not borne out by fact. Although a hardy tree, smoke tolerant and fast growing, very few plants survive beneath its canopy, and it is therefore not recommended for the small garden.

Bark: Pale grey, smooth in young trees, later regularly fissured in a continuous vertical interlacing pattern.

Twigs: Greenish-grey with white lenticels, very stout, somewhat dichotomous and noticeably compressed near the nodes. Winter buds 2 together on opposite sides of stem, very hard, pointed and jet black.

Leaves: Often not unfolding until mid-May. Delicate green, compound-pinnate; exstipulate and long-petiolate. The thin-textured leaflets, 7–15 including terminal, are oblong-lanceolate, about 7.5 cm long and shallowly dentate. The leaf fall is in early autumn and very sudden, a tree may be completely defoliated in a matter of hours.

Flowers: Appear before leaves. Anemophilous. Sexually inconsistent and unpredictable; some trees have both male and female flowers, some bear flowers of one sex only, others bear true flowers with stamens and ovaries, yet again all three may be found on the same tree or branch; any one tree or branch may not produce the same type of flower in consecutive years. Flowers are conspicuous but unimpressive, forming clusters arising from the sides of leaf buds near tips of young shoots and have neither calyx nor corolla. Male clusters are purple then brown; females greenish.

Fruit: Ripe in October. A samara or key, in drooping bunches. Each key consists of a twisted, linear-oblong scale with a notch at the tip. Enclosed is a single seed at the base. Green at first, then brown.

A Bark, Common Ash.
B Flowers ♂, Common Ash.
C Fruit and leaf, Common Ash.

Oleaceae
Common Privet—*Ligustrum vulgare* L.

Description
The Common Privet is a sub-evergreen shrub, 1–3 m high with a straggling habit. The wiry, slender branchlets arch over and root where they reach the ground, forming, in time, large thickets.

Common Privet (tree)

Timber
None as such; wood white, hard and horny. In parts of continental Europe the shoots are used in basket-making and the twigs as tanning agents.

Range and Habitat
Indigenous and locally common on calcareous substrates throughout temperate Europe. In Britain, native as far north as N. Lancashire and Durham and found in open woodland and hedgerows, especially of coastal areas. Very tolerant of polluted atmospheres and shade.

Common Privet (shrub)

Related Trees
The species most frequently met with as a garden hedge is the Oval-leaved Privet, *L. ovalifolium* Hassk., which is fully evergreen with oval or oval-elliptic leaves, of erect and stiff habit, and was introduced from Japan in 1877. The Golden Privet, 'Aureo-marginatum', is a cultivar of *L. ovalifolium*. The Shining Privet, *L. lucidum* Aiton, is the handsomest of the privets, evergreen, dense and erect, bearing long-pointed glossy dark green leaves and lilac-like spreading panicles of creamy-white flowers. Introduced to Europe in 1794, it is known as the Woa Tree.

Associated Macro-fungi
None specific. Often attacked by *Armillaria mellea* (Fries) Kumm., Honey Fungus, especially when growing in acid soils and deprived of lime.

Associated Insects
Lepidoptera—Moths: *Sphinx ligustri* L., Privet Hawk Moth; *Trichopteryx polycommata* Denis & Schiff., Barred Tooth-striped; *Apeira syringaria* L.,

Lilac Beauty; *Clepsis consimilana* Hübn., larvae feed on leaves. *Exapate congelatella* Clerck, larvae in spun shoots. *Pseudargyrotoza conwagana* F., larvae feed on seeds. *Caloptilia syringella* F., larvae in mines, later in rolled leaves. *Adela croesella* Scop., larvae in flat, earth-covered case on fallen leaves. **Hymenoptera**—Sawflies: *Macrophya punctumalbum* L., larvae on leaves.

General Information
The berries are very poisonous to humans, although John Loudon (1783–1843) stated that the oil from them may be used for culinary purposes, also as lamp fuel and in the making of soap. The name *Ligustrum* is derived from the Latin verb 'ligo', to bind.

Bark: Greyish-brown and smooth.

Twigs: Young shoots smooth, green to brown with minute white markings; later smooth, dark brown and wiry. Buds sub-opposite, ovate and brown.

Leaves: Almost evergreen. Opposite, elliptical-lanceolate, 2–6.5 cm long, margin entire. Glabrous, polished green above and lighter green beneath. Petiole short. Autumn tints purplish to orange-brown, many leaves fall during winter.

Flowers: June–July. Bisexual, entomophilous. Funnel-shaped, sickly smelling, white with 4 petals which turn reddish-brown, borne in a densely-panicled, straight-shafted cyme, 2.5–7.5 cm long. Attractive to many flying insects.

Fruit: Ripen November and persist throughout winter when they provide food for passerine birds. A globular, 2-celled berry with oily flesh 8 mm in diameter, green then glossy purple-black; seeds ovoid.

A Leaves, Common Privet.
B Flowers, Common Privet.
C Berries, Common Privet.

Caprifoliaceae
Elder or Bourtree—*Sambucus nigra* L.

Elder

Description
Depending on where it grows—and it grows almost anywhere—the Elder may be seen as an irregular, straggling, deciduous bush with several stems from a common base, or, especially on rich soil, as a quite sizeable tree. As a tree, it can grow up to 6 m high with a girth of up to 60 cm, or exceptionally 1.5 m. In the first few years of its life it grows at a tremendous rate, but it does not live to a great age.

Timber
Yellowish-white. Hard, heavy and close grained. Useful for the manufacture of small durable articles such as tool handles, spoons, meat skewers, etc.

Range and Habitat
Native throughout Europe and N. Africa and common in most parts of Britain. Elder will grow in almost any situation, even under beech trees or on the tops of disused chimney stacks, but shows a preference for a moist but well-drained substrate high in nitrogen content.

Related Trees
The variety 'Lacineata', with cut leaves, occurs as a cultivar. The Red-berried Elder, *S. racemosa* L., which has greenish-yellow flowers and scarlet fruit, native to central Europe, occurs in Britain as an alien. The larger Blueberry Elder, *S. coerulea*, is found in the Pacific Northwest of N. America.

Associated Macro-fungi
Hirneola auricula-judae (St Amans) Berk., Jew's Ear, which is common; and *Agrocybe cylindracea* (DC. ex Fries) Maire. Both are edible.

Associated Insects
Lepidoptera—*Ourapteryx sambucaria* L., the Swallow-tailed Moth, larvae feed openly on leaves. *Eurrhypara coronata* Hufn., larvae in spun fold on underside of leaf. **Hymenoptera**—Sawflies: *Macrophya albicincta* Schrank., larvae on leaves and flowers.

General Information
Traditionally the tree from which Judas hanged himself; also said to be the timber of which Christ's cross was made. In the past, and to a lesser extent today, all parts of this tree were used by herbalists for healing various afflictions, e.g. the bark for dropsy, flowers and fruit (rich in vitamin C) concocted into wine for coughs and colds, and the crushed leaves, which have a peculiar fragrance, for poultices. John Evelyn (1620–1706) was full of praise for this tree, saying that if all its medicinal properties were known, people could be cured of any ailment or injury. However, in another statement he complains that the scent is very noxious to the air, and that in a certain house in Spain surrounded by elders, most of the inhabitants became diseased and died, but when all the trees were removed the place became healthy and wholesome. The foliage as food is ignored by most animals. Once established the tree is difficult to eradicate and these days is more often than not regarded as a weed tree in the garden.

Bark: Greyish-brown, deeply fissured and corky, often cracking and breaking away from the trunk and branches.

Twigs: Stout, greenish-grey, then grey, with many prominent brownish lenticels. Branchlets angular with internal white pith. Buds green, naked and insignificant with few scales at the base.

Leaves: Pinnate with a terminal leaflet, ovate to lanceolate, finely but distinctly dentate and up to 9 cm long. Normally light green but often yellowish; this is probably due to nitrogen deficiency. Stipules small or absent.

Flowers: June and July. Creamy-white and bisexual, 5 mm across in flat-topped terminal clusters on 5 radiating primary stalks. These inflorescences can be as much as 30 cm across, but are usually about half that size. They are strong-scented (unpleasant to some), the pollen is plentiful. The stigma and anthers mature together and the flowers are probably more often self-pollinated than cross-pollinated although they are visited by many insects.

Fruit: The cream-coloured ovaries quickly develop into numerous green drupes (elderberries) which hold the seeds; they ripen in late August and September and by that time are soft, juicy and purplish-black. Very attractive to birds which aid seed dispersal.

A Bark Elder **B** Flowers Elder.
C Berries, Elder.

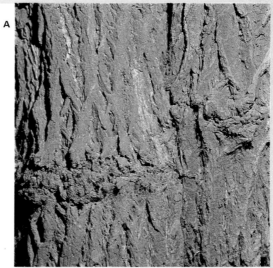

Caprifoliaceae
Guelder Rose—*Viburnum opulus* L.

Guelder Rose

Description
The Guelder Rose is an attractive, open, spreading, deciduous shrub, at most about 3.5 m high, but normally only half that height. In late spring and early summer it is bedecked in green and white, whilst in autumn it is adorned with purplish-crimson foliage and glistening red berries which persist long after leaf-fall. A berry-less variety which is often planted in gardens is aptly called the snowball tree on account of its ball-shaped clusters of sterile, white flowers.

Timber
Unsubstantial and little used.

Range and Habitat
Native throughout Europe and locally common in Britain. Chiefly in copses and hedgerows, preferring damp, fertile soils.

Related Trees
The viburnums comprise a large genus of the temperate northern hemisphere and include American Blackhaw, *V. prunifolium* L., Nannyberry, *V. lentago* L. (also of N. America) and *V. fragrans* Bunge a Chinese, winter-flowering species. Laurustinus, *V. tinus* L., is another winter-flowering species but this is evergreen and originates in the Mediterranean region. The oblong-ovate leaves are opposite, pointed, dark glossy green, glabrous above and downy on veins beneath. These show off the white blossoms which have a pleasant scent. The fruits are blue at first then become black. A Korean species, *V. carlesii* Hemsl., bears pink buds opening into large, white, sweet-scented clusters in April and May. All the above plus many more *Viburnum* species are suitable for garden planting, but are not likely to be found in the wild in Britain other than as escapes.

Associated Macro-fungi
None specific.

Associated Insects on Viburnum spp.
Lepidoptera—Moths: *Acleris schalleriana* L., larvae in twisted leaves. *Coleophora ahenella* Hein., larvae in case on upperside of leaf. *Phyllonorycter lantanella* Schrank, larvae in mine on underside of leaf. **Coleoptera**—Leaf beetle: *Pyrrhalta viburni* Payk., larvae feed openly on leaves. **Homoptera**—Aphid: *Aphis viburni* Scop., form black masses on upper shoots and flowers. **Hymenoptera**—Sawflies: *Tenthredo livida* L.; *T. vespa* Retz.

General Information
The ripe berries emit an offensive odour, but it is said that in Sibera they are mixed with honey and flour to make an edible paste. It is also known as Cranberry Tree, Dog Rowan, Water or Dog Elder and is a useful ornamental for the garden.

Bark: None as such.

Twigs: Glabrous, angular, greenish-grey to reddish-brown. Leaf buds yellowish-green and wrapped in scales. Stipules slender and pointed.

Leaves: Unfold April–May. Maple-like, 5–9 cm long, in opposite pairs. Normally 3-lobed, smooth and deeply dentate. Green at first then bright crimson-purple in autumn.

Flowers: Appear June and July. In uniform, almost flat-topped corymbs 5–9 cm across, comprising 2 rows: the inner with massed creamy-white, fertile flowers 6 cm across, the outer consisting of looser, much larger and conspicuously white, 5-petalled, sterile flowers which attract insects.

Fruit: Almost round berries with 1-seeded stone. Green at first, ripening to a translucent red; beautiful to the eye but nauseous to the taste.

A Habit, Guelder Rose. **B** Flowers, Guelder Rose. **C** Berries, Guelder Rose.

Caprifoliaceae
Wayfaring Tree—*Viburnum lantana* L.

Wayfaring Tree

Description
The Wayfaring Tree is a low, deciduous shrub or very small tree, occasionally attaining a height of 6 m. It bears slender, mealy, pliant stems which branch out in angled pairs from a common point on previous growth. Because the tree is usually many-stemmed from ground level, there is no trunk in the usual sense of the word. In winter, the brown twigs with their large, terminal, naked buds, are distinctive.

Timber
Unsubstantial, of no commercial consequence.

Range and Habitat
Native to Europe from Belgium southwards, also N. Africa. In Britain it is native, but local in the wild state, growing in hedgerows scrub and open woodland, on chalk and limestone, chiefly in S. and S.E. England and parts of Wales. It is also found sparingly on limestone as far north as Lancashire and Yorkshire. Elsewhere introduced.

Associated Macro-fungi
None specific in Britain.

Associated Insects
See under Guelder Rose.

General Information
Twigs are used for making bird-lime. John Gerard (1545–1612), the well known botanist and writer, gave the tree its common English name. He called it the Wayfaring Tree because, he said, 'it is ever on the road'. John Loudon (1783–1843), the Scottish horticultural writer, stated that 'in Germany the young shoots are employed in basket making and for tying faggots and other packages, and older shoots for the stems of tobacco-pipes'. The berries are used in Switzerland to make ink. English local names include Cotton-tree, Lithewort, Mealy Tree, Whip Crop, and Twist-wood, the latter, because ploughboys twisted the stems into handles for whips. In the past the leaves have been used to make various concoctions, including a gargle for loose teeth and sore throats, a hair conditioner and a dark dye.

Bark: None as such.

Twigs: Tough, slender and densely covered in scale-like pubescence. Buds large and naked.

Leaves: Unfold April–May. Ovate, cordate at the base, 5–12 cm long, margin finely dentate. Wrinkled, soft and velvety above; very pubescent with prominent venation beneath. Petiole pubescent, rather short and without glands. Autumn tint deep red.

Flowers: May–June. Creamy-white, small, 8 mm in diameter and perfect. Borne in a dense, flat topped or rounded, terminal corymbs 6–10 cm across. Stamens 5, petals 5.

Fruit: An ovate-oblong berry, 8 mm in diameter, borne in clusters, ripening unevenly from greenish-yellow through red to purplish-black, from July to September. Seed has a ventral groove.

A Habit, Wayfaring Tree.
B Flowers, Wayfaring Tree.
C Berries, Wayfaring Tree.

Taxaceae
Yew—*Taxus baccata* L.

Yew

Irish Yew

Description
A full-grown Yew may be anywhere between 5 and 15 m in height, and, exceptionally, more. It is dull green in colour and conical or round in outline with stout spreading branches densely clad with leafy twigs. The trunk is very variable in length, girth and shape. When the tree has attained its full height, it throws new shoots from the base which develop and thicken, eventually coalescing with the main trunk. Thus the bole becomes a massive, squat, irregularly buttressed column of enormous girth, not uncommonly 6–9 m and often rotted at the centre. Due to this habit of growth and hollowing, the age of really old yews can only be estimated. However, it is known to be the longest lived of all native European trees and may live up to 2000 years.

Timber
Reddish-brown, close grained, exceedingly durable and elastic. Used in the furniture and small tool industries. Once upon a time provided staves for the making of long-bows. Excellent for substantial long-lasting fence posts. Burns well.

Range and Habitat
Yews are native across the northern hemisphere, where about six species are found, all very similiar in character. *T. baccata* is the indigenous yew of Europe, N. Africa and Asia Minor. In Britain it occurs naturally in chalky or limestone areas, but has been planted and has thrived almost nationwide over many centuries.

Related Trees
Varieties include the Irish Yew, 'Fastigiata', bearing erect branches with leaves set round the stems and not in 2 rows as in the type form, and the Westfelton Yew, 'Dovastoniana', which has a drooping habit.

Associated Macro-fungi:
Very few. **Terrestrial**—*Boletus tridentinus* Bres. **Lignicolous**—occasionally *Laetiporus sulphureus* (Fries) Murr., Sulphur Polypore.

Associated Insects
Very few, but the dipteron gall midge *Cecidomyia taxi* Inchb. is common and attacks the terminal buds.

General Information
Yews are slow growing and excellent for topiary work, making ideal hedges provided they are planted in places inaccessible to browsing animals. The foliage, especially when cut and wilted, is deadly poisonous to animals unless they are accustomed to it from birth. The tree is sombre, allows no sunlight to reach the ground beneath it, and so no green plants grow there. Often planted in British church-yards, especially in bygone days, probably as a symbol of 'everlasting life' or maybe 'mourning'; truly a tree surrounded by superstition.

Bark: Reddish-brown with a purple cast, fibrous and thin with pieces periodically flaking off.

Twigs: Fine, tough and flexible, terminating in small leafy buds.

Leaves: Evergreen. Linear and tapering abruptly to a sharp point, they are set spirally in two rows along the shoots. Dark green above, dull green beneath. Petioles very short, appear rosy under a lens.

Flowers and fruits: Almost always dioecious. The male flowers are globular and about 6 mm in diameter, each consisting of small numbers of stamens with surrounding scales at the base. They form profusely in the autumn on the underside of the shoots and mature between February and April when they shed copious amounts of yellowish pollen. Female flowers in winter are no more than pin-head size and solitary

under the shoots. Later the encircling green aril appears and by autumn almost covers the now blackening ovule and quickly becomes fleshy and red. This sweet-tasting mucilaginous aril is the only non-poisonous part of the tree.

A Bark Yew. **B** Flowers ♂ Yew. **C** Fruit Yew.

Pinaceae
Noble Fir—*Abies procera* Rehd.

Noble Fir

Common
Silver Fir

Giant Fir

Description
As its English name implies, this is one of the most beautiful of the silver firs (*Abies*). When young, the tree is narrowly conical and slow growing, but after the first 15 years or so it grows quite quickly and develops a noticeably tapering trunk with, if open grown, a broad, flat crown. The foliage is bluish-green with a distinct silvery sheen, the dense needles sweeping upwards. In its native N.W. America this tree towers to over 75 m and lives to over 400 years, but in Europe a mature height of 35 m is usual.

Timber
Light yellow to brownish, hard, light, fairly strong, close grained and not very durable. Suitable for constructional work, joists, flooring, interior joinery, sounding boards for musical instruments, provision boxes etc. For outside uses the wood is best treated with a preservative. Makes good fuel.

Range and Habitat
Native to rocky slopes of Washington and Oregon in N. America; introduced to Europe between 1825 and 1830. Quite common in parks and large gardens, but few plantations are seen, and only at high elevations are they commercially successful. Rootfirm and suitable for shelter belts, shade tolerant, does not thrive in polluted atmospheres. Prefers deep loams, but will subsist on heavy clays.

Related Trees
The Common Silver Fir, *A. alba* Mill., is native to the steep mountainous regions of central Europe and has, in the past, been extensively planted elsewhere. It was introduced to Britain around 1603, but is rarely planted nowadays. Leaves dark green above, two white bands beneath, and notched at the tip. Cones smaller, narrower and more conic than those of the Noble Fir. The Giant or Grand Fir, *A. grandis* Lindl., native to western N. America, was introduced to Britain in 1831–32. It is the fastest growing of all the introduced trees in Europe, with many specimens over 55 m tall and still growing. Leaves bright green, soft, deeply grooved beneath with two white bands; odour of oranges when crushed. Cones small, bracts not visible.

Associated Macro-fungi
None specific in Britain.

Associated Insects on Abies spp.
Lepidoptera—Moth: *Epinotia nigricana* Herr.-Schaeff., larvae in buds of *A. alba*. **Homoptera**—Aphids: *Adelges piceae* Ratz., on many species of *Abies*, including *Abies nobilis*. *Adelges nusslini* Boern., recorded from *Abies pectinata* and *Abies nordmanniana*.

General Information
Noble Fir is also known in N. America as Red Fir and Oregon Larch. It is very popular in Denmark for Christmas Trees.

Bark: Grey or purplish, smooth, often with resin blisters; older trees develop long, vertical, shallow fissures.

Twigs: Orange-brown, finely pubescent, becoming dark purplish-brown. Winter buds round, resinous, small and purplish.

Leaves: Evergreen. Bluish-green, 1–4 cm long, dense, flat, grooved and leathery with rounded apex. When shed they leave circular scars on the shoots.

Flowers: May. Monoecious, anemophilous. Male catkins solitary, but crowded, in leaf axils, bud-like and deep purple. Female flowers cylindric, usually scattered fairly high-up on tree, 4–5 cm long, yellowish-green with slender, orange-tipped scales.

Fruit: A large cone, 20–25 cm long, 8 cm broad; erect on shoots, cylindrical and bluntly rounded at both ends; purplish-

brown with many long-dentate,
downward-pointing, green bracts.
Altogether brown when fully ripe in
September, eventually breaking up,
leaving the slender core on the tree.
Two-winged seeds, 8 mm long, beneath
each scale. Small trees only 4.5 m high,
may bear cones.

A Bark, Noble Fir.
B Underside of needles, Noble Fir.
C Cone, Noble Fir.

Pinaceae
Douglas or Green Douglas Fir—*Pseudotsuga menziesii* (Mirb.) Franco

Douglas Fir

Description
Open grown Douglas Firs are typically single-stemmed and narrowly conical, bearing light, whorled branches almost to the ground until they are cleaned or clean themselves. The lower branches sweep downwards, but the uppermost are slightly ascending. This is one of the fastest growing and tallest of trees: a specimen felled on Vancouver Island at the end of the last century was measured at 127 m and there are trees in Europe (including Britain) now over 55 m high. In America, its native country, it is said to survive up to 750 years.

Timber
When imported, known as Oregon pine or British Columbian pine. Sapwood yellowish, heartwood pinkish-brown or darker, coarse textured, straight grained and resinous. Heartwood fairly strong and moderately durable; sapwood not at all durable. Slow-grown timber from older trees makes the best material. Used for constructional work, joinery, plywood panelling, sleepers, pit-props, packing cases etc.

Range and Habitat
Native to western N. America, from British Columbia to Mexico, forming large forests in many areas. Seeds sent to Britain in 1827 since when it has been planted more and more extensively in forests throughout Europe. Thrives best on deep, lightish soils, yet will subsist on low pH, sandy or clay substrates. Needs a moist mild climate to succeed and is prone to frost damage. Very fast growing trees are often blown down.

Related Trees
The Colorado or Blue Douglas Fir, *P. glauca* Mayr., regarded by many as a variety of *P. menziesii*, bears shorter, bluish leaves, has leaden grey bark, and smaller cones with outward pointing bracts. It is a hardy and smaller tree in all respects, planted in Britain and Europe only as an ornamental.

Associated Macro-fungi
None specific in Britain and Europe.

Associated Insects
Coleoptera—Weevil: *Strophosomus capitatus* DeGeer (*obesus* Marsh.), also on other trees including pine and oak.
Homoptera—Aphid: *Adelges cooleyi* Gill., also on Sitka Spruce.
Hymenoptera—*Megastigmus spermotrophus* Wachtl, Douglas Fir Seed Fly, larvae within seeds during summer and winter, pupate following spring.

General Information
In America, the timber was formerly in demand for ships' masts and spars. It is not a tree for the small garden.

Bark: Dark, smooth and greyish-green when young; later smooth, decidedly purplish and resin blistered; finally corky, greyish-brown, ribbed, with orange-grey channels.

Twigs: Young shoots pale green, minutely pubescent, becoming grey. Buds distinctive, slender, fusiform and similar to those of Common Beech, about 13 mm long, with brown scales and not resinous.

Leaves: Evergreen. Soft, in various shades of green with 2 silvery bands on underside, 2–3 cm long, blunt, flat and linear, broadly in 2 ranks. When shed they leave a slightly raised oval scar. Crushed foliage has a sweet resinous scent.

Flowers: April–May. Monoecious, anemophilous. Male catkins on underside of previous years shoots, bud-like, ovoid, pale yellow with pollen. Female flowers greenish, ovoid, at tips of lateral branches, about 1.8 cm long.

Fruit: A narrowly elongated, pendulous cone, about 8 cm long, ripening green to brown in autumn, but not breaking up. The 3-clawed bract-scales project downwards beyond the cone-scales, the middle claw being longest. Seed 1.5 cm in diameter, reddish-brown with dark brown wing, and 2 to each scale.

A Bark (young tree), Douglas Fir.
B Bark (mature tree), Douglas Fir.
C Cones, Douglas Fir.

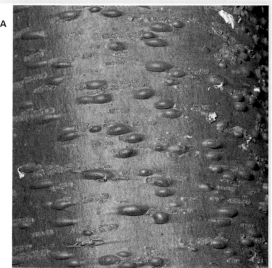

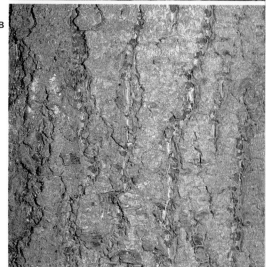

Pinaceae
Western Hemlock—*Tsuga heterophylla* (Raf.) Sarg.

Western
Hemlock

Eastern
Hemlock

Description
The Western Hemlock is an elegant, fast-growing, windfirm, shade tolerant, single-stemmed, evergreen tree. It has a very cylindrical trunk with a buttressed base, and a spire-like crown with drooping main leader. The sweeping, ascending or horizontal branches bear the thick foliage in an attractive manner. It is one of the most beautiful of trees, especially when open grown as a specimen.

Timber
Sapwood and heartwood creamy or pale brown, soft and light, straight grained, finely textured, strong but not durable, and prone to discolour. In all a valuable, fast-growing timber suitable for flooring, panelling, boxes, general joinery and pulp. Bark is rich in tannin.

Range and Habitat
Native to western N. America from S.W. Alaska to N. California. Introduced into Britain in 1851. Now popular as a forest tree, also grown as an ornamental. Not conservative as to soil requirements, but thrives best on deep moist loams in areas of fairly high rainfall, i.e. western Britain.

Related Trees
The Eastern Hemlock, *T. canadensis* (L.) Carr., native to north-eastern N. America, introduced into Britain in 1736, is a tree with short trunk quickly dividing into several substantial ascending branches, and only rarely single-stemmed. Buds ovoid; leaves tapered not parallel sided, placed in 2–3 rows, one row on topside of shoot twisted and flattened to show white-banded underside; cones similar to those of Western Hemlock but smaller. As a timber tree much inferior to the Western Hemlock. The Mountain Hemlock, *T. mertensiana* (Bongard) Carr., is native in N. America from Alaska to the Sierra Nevada and was introduced to Britain in 1854. It has

been known to attain a height of 30 m in Britain, but is usually less than this and quite often small. The foliage is silvery-green and pendulous, with the leaves set radially and pointing forward. The crown is narrow and the leading shoot drooping. The cones are larger than those of other hemlocks, spruce-like and pendulous from high up the tree. Not a common tree in Britain, more likely to be seen in central Scotland than anywhere else.

Associated Macro-fungi
None specific in Britain and Europe.

Associated Insects
None specific in Britain and Europe.

General Information
Crushed foliage has an aromatic smell, said to resemble that of the Hemlock (Umbelliferae), hence the common name. North American Indians made a type of bread from the inner bark of the Western Hemlock, and fish hooks from the roots. Good hedge material.

Bark: Young trees smooth and purplish-brown; later greyish-green, becoming shiny silvery-brown and breaking up into irregular flaky plates; old trees darker and shallowly fissured.

Twigs: Young shoots brown above, lighter beneath, ribbed and bearing coarse, curly, brownish hairs. Buds brown, small, round and blunt. Bare twigs have rounded humps.

Leaves: Evergreen. Vary in length on same shoots from 5 to 18 mm, parallel sided, slightly tapering to a rounded apex. Well spaced in rows, lower leaves longer than upper ones, and at right-angles to the shoot; upper leaves point forwards. All dark shiny green above, with 2 broad, bluish-white bands beneath; short stalked.

Flowers: April–May. Monoecious, anemophilous. Male catkins dense, in leaf axils, small, 3mm long, globular,

crimson then yellowish with pollen.
Female flowers terminal on shoots,
ovoid, reddish-purple, similar in size to
males.

Fruit: Borne freely, a small pendulous
cone, bronze-green ripening through
purple to pale brown, about 2.5 cm long
and bluntly ovoid. Remain intact on
tree for many months after shedding
seed.

A Bark, Western Hemlock.
B Young cones, Western Hemlock.
C Mature cones, Western Hemlock.

Pinaceae
Norway or Common Spruce—*Picea abies* (L.) Karst.

Norway
Spruce

Description
The Norway Spruce is a narrowly conical, graceful, not rootfirm, evergreen tree with light, whorled branches. The upper branches ascend slightly, whilst the rest are more or less horizontal. Open grown trees retain their lower branches but in mature plantations, the trees are often clean to over half their height. They are at first slow-growing, but after 10 years or so the growth becomes rapid. Mature trees vary in height, according to the geographical location, from 24 m in N. Europe to 60 m in central Europe. Norway spruces are old at 200 years.

Timber
White to pale buff. Even grained, soft, light, tough and elastic, but not very durable; quality influenced by climate and situation. There are a multitude of uses which include, packing cases, pulp for paper, ladder sides, interior construction, sleepers, and joinery, furniture, table tops, and certain musical string instruments. Known as white deal and furnishes Burgundy pitch.

Range and Habitat
Native to the mountainous regions of northern and central Europe, and Asia. Introduced to Britain sometime before the middle of the 16th century. Succeeds best on fertile and moist loams but will tolerate clays and sands; acid, peaty soils are not to its liking. Even when close grown, this shallow-rooted tree is not at all windfirm.

Related Trees
There are many cultivars of Norway Spruce, the dwarf varieties being most suitable for small gardens: 'Clanbrassilliana' is a low, dense, round bush, which only grows about 1 m in 30 years; 'Repens' is a low creeping cultivar suitable for rockeries. Oriental Spruce, *P. orientalis* (L.) Link, is native to Caucasus and Asia Minor and quite

common as an introduced tree in Britain and Europe. It is a densely branched, conical tree, easily identified by its leaves, which are the shortest of all the spruce species being only 0.5–1 cm long.

Associated Macro-fungi on Spruces
See under Sitka Spruce.

Associated Insects on Spruces
Lepidoptera—Moths: *Lymantria monacha* L., Black Arches Moth, recorded in Britain from oak, and other trees, including apple and pine, is primarily a pest of spruce and known to be so on the Continent; it occurs in the southern half of England (somewhat locally) but does not seem to be a pest there. *Dioryctria abietella* Denis & Schiff., larvae in cones. *Zeiraphera ratzeburgiana* Ratz., larvae in new shoots. *Epinotia pygmaena* Hübn.; *E. tedella* Clerck; *Cydia strobilella* L., larvae in cones causing resinous exudations. *Argyresthia glabratella* Zell., larvae in shoots. *Thera variata* Denis & Schiff., Spruce Carpet, larvae on leaves. *Aphelia viburnana* Denis & Schiff.; *Eupithecia nanata* Hübn., Narrow-winged Pug, normally feed on *Vaccinium* etc. *E. abietaria* Goeze, Cloaked Pug, larvae in cones feeding on immature seeds. *E. tantillaria* Boisd., Dwarf Pug. **Coleoptera**—*Pityogenus chalcographus* L.; *Ips typographus* L.; *Polygraphus polygraphus* L., larvae on wood beneath bark. *Pissodes pini* L., larvae in cambium layer between bark and wood. *Strophosomus melanogrammus* Foerst., larvae on roots, adults on leaves. *Callidium violaceum* L.; *Molorchus minor* L., larvae live in wood. **Homoptera**—Aphids: *Elatobium abietinum* Walk., Green Spruce Aphid (formerly *Neomyzaphis abietina*), wingless forms on needles throughout the year, winged forms occur in summer. *Adelges cooleyi* Gill.; *A. abietus* L.; *A. laricis* Vall. (=*A. strobilobius* Kaltenb.), generally form cone-like structures (pseudocone galls) which

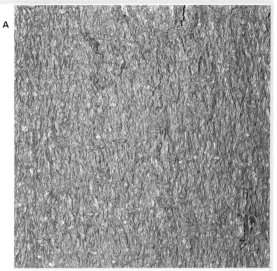

mature in summer; adults fly to various other conifers where they feed but form no galls. **Hymenoptera**—Sawflies: *Pristiphora saxesenii* Hart.; *P. abietina* Chris.; *P. compressa* Hart.

General Information
Fossil evidence shows that spruce species grew in the British Isles millions of years ago. Norway Spruce is familiar to most British families as the species commonly used for Christmas trees.

Bark: Thin, brown and smooth in young trees; later breaking up into irregular scales which are shed. Old trees darker, resolving into small, round plates.

Twigs: Reddish-brown, grooved, and glabrous but rough (caused by the peg-like projections). Buds conical, dark brown, not resinous, about 5 mm long.

Leaves: Evergreen. Acicular on peg-like projections, which remain on twigs when leaves fall or are removed. Dark green, quadrangular, sharply pointed, evenly encircling shoots, and pointing towards apex (resembling a flue-brush). Each leaf about 2 cm long, and persists for a number of years.

Flowers: May. Monoecious, anemophilous. Male catkins 1 cm long, situated singly in leaf axils, but clustered at the end of young shoots; yellow when shedding pollen. Female flowers sessile, erect, bud-like, at tips of previous years shoots; purplish-red, soon turning green and leaning over, eventually becoming pendulous.

Fruit: A cylindrical, semi-pendulous, gently tapering cone, 12–15 cm long, 4 cm broad; ripening shiny brown in the same autumn, and falling not shattering. Cone-scales numerous, thin, and overlap loosely. Two small, brown, winged seeds at base of each scale.

A Bark, Norway Spruce.
B Flowers ♀ (left), ♂ (right), Norway Spruce.
C Mature cones, Norway Spruce.

Pinaceae
Sitka Spruce—*Picea sitchensis* (Bongard) Carr.

Sitka Spruce

Description
The Sitka Spruce is a rapid-growing, graceful, windfirm, evergreen tree. When open grown it is narrowly conical at first, broadening later, but always with a long spire. The higher branches are ascending, whilst the lower ones are horizontal or directed downwards, and the tapered trunk often bears sprouts. In Britain, the trees reach over 40 m in height with trunk diameters of 1.5 m or more, but in its native America there are trees of over 60 m with trunks in excess of 4 m in diameter. At 50 years old, good trees are around 30 m high. The tree has a silvery appearance and the foliage is harsh and prickly.

Timber
In appearance similar to Norway Spruce but harder. Usually straight grained, soft, light and fairly strong, not durable. Best timber for pulp; other uses as for Norway Spruce.

Range and Habitat
Native to the coastal areas of western N. America, from N. California to Alaska. Introduced to Britain in 1831. Now very popular as a timber tree, especially in western Britain, due to its quick growth related to volume of timber, and its tolerance to various substrates and altitudes. Prefers moist deep soils where rainfall is fairly high.

Related Trees
The Serbian Spruce, *P. omorika* (Pančić) Purkyne, was widely distributed in Europe before the last Ice Age. Native only on limestone in the Drina Valley, Yugoslavia, it also thrives on acid soils when planted, and is very tolerant of air pollution and frost. Becoming more popular as a timber tree, or as an ornamental in Britain and N. Europe. A straight, very narrow, spire-like tree up to 30 m, with reddish-brown flaky bark; young shoots pubescent; leaves about 2 cm long, noticeably flattened, light green then blue green with 2 white bands on underside. Cones small, fusiform and pointed.

Associated Macro-fungi on Spruces
Terrestrial—*Amanita porphyria* (Fries) Secr.; *Agaricus sylvatica* Schaeff. ex Secr.; *Boletus edulis* (subsp. *trisporus*) Duncan & Watl.; *Boletus badius* Fries; *Clitocybe flaccida* (Fries) Kumm.; *Collybia dryophila* (Fries) Kumm.; *Cortinarius sanguineus* (Fries) Fries; *C. semisanguineus* (Fries) Gill.; *Cystoderma amianthinum* (Fries) Fay.; *Fayodia bisphaerigera* (J. Lange) Sing.; *Hygrophoropsis aurantiaca* (Fries) Maire; *Inocybe calamistrata* (Fries) Gill.; *Lactarius deterimus* Grög.; *Lyophyllum connatum* (Fries) Sing.; *Marasmius androsaceus* (Fries) Fries; *Micromphale perforans* (Hoff. ex Fries) S. F. Gray; *Mycena adonis* (Fries) S. F. Gray; *M. capillaripes* Peck; *M. vulgaris* (Fries) Kumm.; *Psathyrella caput-medusae* (Fries) Konrad & Maubl.; *Pseudohiatula esculenta* (Wulf. ex Fries) Sing.; *Russula emetica* (Fries) S. F. Gray; *R. queletii* Fries apud Quél.; *R. sardonia* Fries; *Tricholoma flavovirens* (Fries) Lund.; *Tricholoma terreum* (Schaeff. ex Fries) Kumm. **Lignicolous**—*Gymnopilus penetrans* (Fries) Murr.; *Hypholoma capnoides* (Fries) Kumm.; *H. radicosum* J. Lange; *Mycena alcalina* (Fries) Kumm.; *Calocera viscosa* (Fries) Fries; *Heterobasidion annosum* (Fries) Bref.; *Stereum sanguinolentum* (Fries) Fries; *Tremella encephala* Pers. These species are but a few of those which may be found; none can be regarded as truly specific in Britain.

Associated Insects on Spruces
See under Norway Spruce.

General Information
Sitka is the name of a small seaport on Baranoff Island in southern Alaska. Other names for this species in America are Tideland Spruce, Menzies Spruce, and Western Spruce.

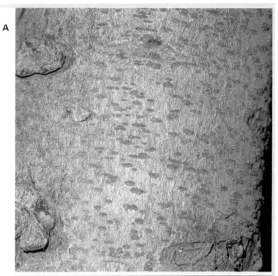

Bark: Grey at first, later purplish or brownish-grey, resolving into irregular flaking plates.

Twigs: Orange-brown when young, grooved, knobbly and glabrous; darker with age. Buds bluntly ovoid, pale brown and resinous.

Leaves: Evergreen. Four-sided, flat, stiff and very sharply pointed; those on topside of shoot pointing forwards, light green at first, then darker and shiny with 2 white bands on underside.

Flowers: May. Monoecious, anemophilous. Male catkins in clusters 2.5–3.5 cm long, yellow to purple. Female catkins 2–5 cm long, red or greenish-red.

Fruit: A cone, 5–10 cm long, ripening pale brown, soft and springy, cylindrical, and blunt at apex. Scales thin, toothed and wavy at the edges.

A Bark, Sitka Spruce.
B & C Cones, Sitka Spruce.

Pinaceae
European Larch—*Larix decidua* Mill.

European
Larch

Description
The European Larch is a rapid-growing, light-demanding, deciduous conifer, between 25 and 35 m in height with girths from 3 to 4.5 m. When open grown, and with reasonable shelter from high winds, it is conical in outline with a single, straight trunk and uniformly downswept, slender branches which arch upwards again at the tips. When close grown in plantations, the lower branches die and fall off at an early age. The larch is a hardy and graceful tree, showing a marked change in seasonal colour. It is mature at 40–50 years; maximum lifetime 200 years.

Timber
Sapwood yellowish and narrow, heartwood reddish-brown, coarse, straight grained, strong and durable. Superior to most softwoods and highly esteemed. Used extensively for fence posts, lap-fencing, hop-poles, rustic work, pit timber, scaffolding, planking for boats, and piling; in fact wherever a timber is required to withstand the test of time and alternation of wet and dry conditions it is hardly bettered. The bark is used for tanning, and the trunk furnishes Venice turpentine.

Range and Habitat
Native to the mountainous regions of central and southern Europe, and forest forming. Introduced into Britain during the 17th century, and has been planted extensively over the years. Although larches are essentially trees of mountainous regions and prefer alluvial sandy loam, they will thrive on most well-drained fertile substrates if given adequate space to develop.

Related Trees
The Japanese Larch, *L. kaempferi* Carr., is native to Japan, introduced to Britain in 1861 and, because of its resistance to larch cancer, is widely planted. The twigs are dark orange-red to purplish; winter buds resinous; leaves bluish-green, broader than *L. decidua*, with whitish bands beneath. Ripe cone-scales rosette-like, with tips turned outwards and downwards. Dunkeld Larch, *L. x eurolepis* Henry, is a hybrid between *L. decidua* and *L. kaempferi*. It first occurred naturally at Dunkeld early this century. Only first cross hybrids show great vigour, and have definite characteristics. The leaves are bluish-green with grey bands beneath. Ripe cone-scales have spreading tips, but are not curled downwards. Very resistant to disease.

Associated Macro-fungi
Terrestrial—*Hygrophorus bresadolae* Quél.; *Boletus elegans* Fries; *B. aeruginascens* Secr., in mycorrhizal association. Their presence seems to indicate healthy trees. *Tricholoma psammopus* (Kalchb.) Quél. **Lignicolous** —*Armillaria mellea* (Fries) Kumm., Honey Fungus, attacks most species of trees but frequently a serious problem in larch forests. Many other species associated with conifers may be found.

Associated Insects on European and Japanese Larch
Lepidoptera—Moths: *Coleophora laricella* Hübn., larvae in greyish-white cylindrical case. *Cydia deciduana* Steuer, in gall on end of twigs. *Argyresthia laevigella* Herr.-Schaeff., in terminal twigs. *Eupithecia lariciata* Frey., Larch Pug, larvae on foliage (also on spruce). **Homoptera**—Aphid: *Adelges laricis* Vall. (also on some pines). **Hymenoptera**—Sawflies: *Anoplonyx destructor* Bens., sometimes a pest in Britain. *Pristiphora laricis* Hart. and other species of the genus may be pests in some forests. **Diptera**—Gall midge: *Dasyneura laricis* Loew, forms swellings on twigs.

General Information
Although the trees cast little shade when open grown, the ground flora in a larch forest is non-existent.

Bark: Greyish-brown and smooth at first; becoming thick and fibrous, separable into thin layers and broken into deep, longitudinal fissures and scaly ridges.

Twigs: Mainly pendulous, dull straw coloured, knobbly and grooved, otherwise smooth and glabrous. Buds dark brown, cylindrical and stumpy.

Leaves: Unfold March–April. Clustered on woody nodes in bundles of 30–60, or singly on new shoots, 2–4 cm long, very soft and spreading, narrow, parallel-sided, blunt or rounded at apex. Grass green throughout.

Flowers: March–April. Monoecious. Male catkins sessile on young shoots, ovoid, globose, 5–10 mm in diameter, pale green then yellow with pollen. Female flowers (larch roses) cylindrical, erect, blunt and solitary 1.5 cm long, usually rose-pink, becoming darker, then green before ripening.

Fruit: Ripen October–November, remain on tree indefinitely. Barrel-shaped cones 2–3.5 cm long, 2 cm broad, warm brown. Scales persistent, broad and round, tips straight or slightly incurved. Seeds ovate and winged, 2 to each scale, and released the following spring.

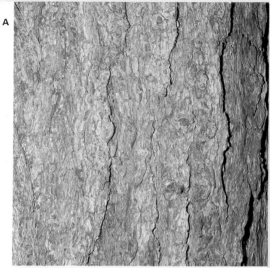

A Bark, European Larch.
B Cones and leaves, European Larch.
C Cones, Japanese Larch.

Pinaceae
Cedar of Lebanon—*Cedrus libani* A. Rich.

Cedar of Lebanon

Deodar

Description
When open grown, the Cedar of
Lebanon is at first a pyramidal, compact
tree with a regular outline. However,
later in life they become very broad,
flat-topped and massive, with round,
rigid branches breaking out
unpredictably from many parts of the
bole; some ascend sharply then flatten
out, others project straight out and then
descend. All the branches terminate in
distinct layers of flat, fan-like, thickly
set branchlets. Trees may attain heights
of 25–35 m with short, sturdy,
buttressed boles of 1.5–3 m in diameter,
and although perpendicular growth is
slow, the girth expands quite rapidly
from 20 years onwards. In Lebanon,
some cedars are said to be over 2000
years old although this may be an
overestimation.

Timber
Sapwood yellowish-white, heartwood
reddish-brown, durable but not very
strong, brittle and subject to shakes,
straight grained, soft and light, easily
worked. Not grown in Europe as a
timber tree, but that which is available
is useful for chests, wardrobes and
other furniture, gates and seed-boxes
etc. Cedar wood is pleasantly fragrant
and repels most insects.

Range and Habitat
Native to the higher areas of Lebanon,
Syria and Turkey, where it is now no
longer common. Introduced to Britain
mid-17th century, and now common as
an amenity tree in cemeteries, parks and
large gardens, not only in Britain but
throughout central and southern
Europe; also in N. America. Not
conservative as to soils but thrives best
in deep, moist, well-drained loams.
Frost hardy, but old, spreading trees are
susceptible to snow-break.

Related Trees
The Deodar, *Cedrus deodara* (Roxb.)
G. Don ex Loud., is native to the
western Himalayas where it forms large
forests. Introduced to Britain in 1831
by the Hon. W. L. Melville, it is similar
to but more graceful than the Cedar of
Lebanon, and, until quite old, retains a
much narrower and regular outline
which is conical with a light spire and
noticeably drooping main leader. The
terminal shoots on branches also droop
considerably and these are densely
pubescent. The leaves are longer than
those of Cedar of Lebanon, and dark
bluish-green with a glaucous bloom.
Indian-grown timber is exceedingly
durable. Planted as an ornamental in
Europe, including Britain, and N.
America. The Atlas Cedar, *C. atlantica*
(Endl.) Carr., native to the mountainous
regions of Algeria and Morocco, has an
erect leader and the terminal shoots of
the rather sparse branches are
ascending. Commonly planted as an
ornamental in Europe and N. America,
where the form *glauca* with attractive
bluish foliage is most often seen, and is
more suitable for smaller gardens than
either the Lebanon or the Indian trees.
Likes lime-rich substrates and
withstands drought conditions.

Associated Macro-fungi
None specific in Britain.

Associated Insects
None specific in Britain.

General Information
In the Middle East the tree is much
revered and respected by the native
peoples. The timber was used in the
construction of Solomon's Temple and
Palace at Jerusalem in Biblical times.
Hindus burn cedar wood as an incense
because of its fragrance.

Bark: Smooth and dark grey at first;
later shallowly networked and
brownish; old trees flaky with deeper,
more pronounced fissures.

Twigs: Pale brown and sparsely
pubescent until second year; new

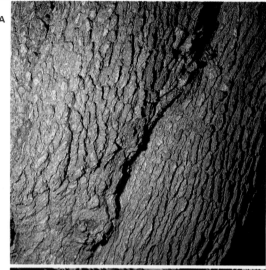

shoots drooping on adult trees. Buds ovoid and brown.

Leaves: Evergreen, each leaf persisting for around 3 years. Borne singly on new growth, but on mature growth in tufts borne on short spurs arranged spirally round the shoots. Each leaf 2–3 cm long, fairly rigid, tapering to a spiny apex. Dark green to bluish-grey.

Flowers: August–October. Monoecious, anemophilous. Rarely produced on trees under 25 years old. Male catkins abundant and conspicuous, mainly at the tops of trees, 1 cm long, green and erect, lengthening to 5 cm, yellow with pollen in autumn. Female flowers smaller and terminal on short spurs, ovoid, bright green, later purplish and expanding.

Fruit: Large, erect, compact, barrel-shaped cone on a short, thick spur; greyish at first, ripening in 2 or 3 years and persisting on the trees even longer, eventually breaking up to release large angular winged seeds. Mature cones 7.5–11.5 cm long, thin-scaled, purplish-brown and somewhat resinous.

A Bark, Cedar of Lebanon.
B Young cones, Cedar of Lebanon.
C Young cones, Deodar. D Bark, Atlas Cedar.

Pinaceae
Scots Pine—*Pinus sylvestris* L.

Scots Pine

Description
The Scots Pine is an evergreen tree, 15–36 m high when mature with girths up to 7 m. At first the tree has a conical outline with a straight stem and annual whorls of short, spreading, light branches, the lower branches soon dying and falling off. Later in life the upper branches thicken and spread outwards, give the tree an attractive appearance with a broad, flat-topped crown or several small crowns at different levels. A few trees have been recorded as living over 300 years, but half that life-span is more general.

Timber
Sapwood yellowish-white, heartwood pale brown or brownish-red, resinous, fairly durable and straight grained. Fast home-grown timber is inferior to the slower-grown Baltic type, both climate and soil conditions considerably affect the quality. Used extensively in the building trade for joists, rafters, flooring, window-frames etc., also pit-props, telegraph poles, gate posts, crates, sleepers and paper pulp.

Range and Habitat
Common and widespread over most of Europe. In Britain indigenous now only in Scotland although once native over much of the country. Today it is planted extensively and naturalised, growing on any but the wettest or very limy substrates. Thrives best on gravelly loam and unlike most conifers will tolerate grassy or weedy situations during infancy. Hardy and windfirm.

Associated Macro-fungi
Auriscalpium vulgare S. F. Gray; *Strobilurus stephanocystis* (Hora) Sing.; *S. tenacellus* (Fries) Sing.; *Baespora myosura* (Fries) Sing., attached to fallen or buried cones. **Terrestrial**—*Amanita muscaria* (Fries) Hook.; *Boletus granulatus* Fries; *B. bovinus* (L.) Fries; *B. variegatus* Sow. ex Fries; *Hygrophorus hypothejus* (Fries) Fries;

Lactarius deliciosus (Fries) S. F. Gray; *L. rufus* (Fries) Fries; *Russula emetica* (Fries) S. F. Gray; *R. caerulea* Fries; *R. consobrina* (Fries) Fries. **Lignicolous** —*Gymnopilus penetrans* (Fries) Murr.; *Tricholomopsis rutilans* (Fries) Sing.; *Calocera viscosa* (Fries) Fries; *Heterobasidion annosum* (Fries) Bref.; *Sparassis crispa* Wulfen ex Fries; *Mycena alcalina* (Fries) Kumm. All the above species may be found on or under other pines.

Associated Insects
Lepidoptera—Moths: *Hyloicus pinastri* L., Pine Hawk; *Panolis flammea* Denis & Schiff., Pine Beauty; *Thera firmata* Hübn., Pine Carpet; *Bupalus piniaria* L., Bordered White, larvae feed on leaves. *Dioryctria abietella* Denis & Schiff., larvae in cones and shoots. *Archips oporana* L.; *Rhyacionia buoliana* Denis & Schiff., larvae on blossom. *Cydia conicolana* Heyl., larvae in cones. **Coleoptera**—Beetles: *Aphideita obliterata* L.; *Anatis ocellata* L., predatory on insects. *Hylobius abietis* L.; *Pissodes pini* L., in roots. *Hylaster ater* Payk., under bark. *Myelophilus piniperda* L., in shoots. *Rhagium bifasciatum* F., larvae bore in decaying timber. **Homoptera**—Leaf-hoppers: *Psylla melanoneura* Foerst. (also on Hawthorn), common on pine during winter. **Hymenoptera**—Sawflies: *Neodiprion sertifer* Geoff.; *Diprion pini* L.; *Microdiprion pallipes* Fallen, larvae on foliage. Wood wasps: *Sirex gigas* L.; *S. cyaneus* F., larvae bore in wood.

General Information
A medicinal oil is extracted from the needles, the tree also yields pitch tar, resin, and turpentine. Dodonaeus, the 16th-century Dutch herbalist wrote, 'The leaves of the Pine healeth green woundes and boyled in vinegar they swage the toothache.' The tree is often referred to, incorrectly, as Scots Fir. Good for wildlife.

Bark: Rough and grey in young trees; with age the bark on the lower part of the tree becomes fissured into pinkish-grey plates; higher on the trunk and on heavy branches it is thin, flaky and rusty red.

Twigs: Young shoots glabrous and pale greenish-brown, becoming finely ribbed and greyish-brown. Buds cylindrical, pointed, rusty red and resinous.

Leaves: Evergreen. In pairs on dwarf branches, twisted and dense, 5–7.5 cm long, shortest on old trees. Bluish-green first year, then dark green; shed in third year.

Flowers: May. Monoecious, anemophilous. Male catkins yellow, fluffy, 8 mm long, in erect, shortly stalked clusters at the base of young shoots, and consisting of numerous stamens which shed copious pale yellow pollen. Female flowers egg-shaped 6 mm long, and reddish, usually 2–3 at the tips of new shoots.

Fruit: Woody cone, full grown and ripening (in its second year) from green to greyish or reddish-brown; 5–8 cm long, ovoid, pointed, short-stalked and pendulous. Seeds winged, 2 on each cone-scale.

A Bark, Scots Pine. **B** Flowers ♂, Scots Pine.
C Mature cones, Scots Pine.

129

Pinaceae
Maritime or Cluster Pine—*Pinus pinaster* Aiton

Maritime Pine

Stone Pine

Description
The Maritime Pine is a rapid-growing, light-demanding, frost-tender, open, evergreen tree up to 36 m high with a trunk diameter of 0.5–1.5 m. The mature tree is round-headed, rather sparsely branched with a clean, frequently bent bole, often up to two-thirds of the tree height. The numerous, clustered, large cones which persist on the branches for years are characteristic of this tree.

Timber
Sapwood pale yellow, heartwood reddish-brown, coarse textured, knotty, resinous and of inferior quality, fairly durable but needs preservative treatment for outside uses. Not grown for timber in Britain, but once imported in large amounts from France for use as pit-props. Other uses include rough joinery, box boards, sleepers, telegraph poles etc. Trees tapped annually for resin produce superior timber.

Range and Habitat
Native to maritime regions of central and western Mediterranean and N. Africa; naturalised and common in coastal areas of France and Portugal. Probably introduced to Britain in late 16th century, common only in sandy areas of southern England, rare elsewhere in the country. Will only thrive on deep neutral or acid, sandy or gravelly substrates in lowland areas.

Related Trees
The Stone or Umbrella Pine, *P. pinea* L., is native to the Mediterranean region, and introduced to Britain some time before 1548 although still uncommon there. Normally a squat tree between 7.5 and 12 m but much taller in some of its native areas. The bole is sturdy and short with long, heavy, straight, ascending branches breaking out from quite low down. The crown is broad and rounded, making 'Umbrella Pine' a fitting descriptive name. Bark orange

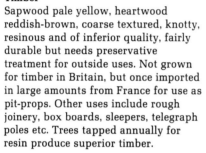

to reddish-brown, resolving into longitudinal plates with grey fissures between; leaves evergreen, single on young trees, later in pairs 12–15 cm long, stout, sharp pointed, and often twisted; cones large and rounded, maturing in three years. The nutritious seeds are cropped and eaten in Italy. The Dwarf Mountain Pine, *P. mugo* Turra, is native to the mountains of central Europe. It is little more than a thicket-forming, straggling shrub bearing dark green, dense foliage and small cones 2–5 cm long. Popular in Britain as a fill-in for landscape areas.

Associated Macro-fungi
None specific in Britain. Many species associated with other pines are likely to be found.

Associated Insects
None specific in Britain. Many species associated with other pines are likely to be found.

General Information
The Maritime Pine is of great commercial importance in France, Corsica, Spain and Portugal as the foremost source of the resin used to make oil of turpentine. The resin is obtained by tapping the trees each summer. The species is also very useful for stabilising sand dunes and for shelter belts near the sea.

Bark: Varying shades of brown and purplish-brown, resolving into irregular elongated plates divided by broad fissures.

Twigs: Pale green with reddish tinge when young; later stout, glabrous, pale to reddish-brown. Buds large, woolly, non-resinous and bright reddish-brown.

Leaves: Evergreen. In pairs, 10–25 cm long, stiff and fleshy, spiny pointed. Pale greyish-green.

Flowers: May–June. Monoecious, anemophilous. Male catkins clustered

on new shoots and yellow in full bloom. Female conelets 4–8, at tips of shoots, ovoid, small and reddish.

Fruit: Very large, almost sessile, persistent cone, up to 22 cm long, often in clusters, cylindric-ovoid, gradually tapering to apex; ripening from purplish-green to bright shiny brown. Umbo ending in a sharp spine.

A Bark, Maritime Pine.
B Young cones, Maritime Pine.
C Mature cone, Maritime Pine.

Pinaceae
Coastal Lodgepole or Beach Pine—*Pinus contorta* Dougl. var. *contorta*

Coastal
Lodgepole
Pine

Corsican Pine

Description
The Coastal Lodgepole Pine is a very variable, exceedingly hardy, evergreen tree, similar in appearance to the Scots Pine. It may reach 27 m in height and generally has a straight single or sometimes forked stem, bearing short, twisted branches. The lowest branches are descending and the higher ones are ascending but all tend to arch upwards. Although the foliage is dense, in general the tree is rather open.

Timber
Sapwood pale brown, heartwood darker, fairly strong and similar in usage to Scots Pine. Now a popular timber tree in parts of Britain and Europe where most other conifers fail to thrive.

Range and Habitat
Native to coastal areas of western N. America from Alaska to California. Introduced to Britain in the 19th century but remained uncommon and unpopular until about the 1950s. Thrives on moist peaty or mineral soils. Large areas of poor, eroding moorland in northern and western Britain have been successfully planted with Lodgepole Pine. It is tolerant of air pollution, frost and wet, windy climates.

Related Trees
The Inland Lodgepole Pine, *P. contorta* var. *latifolia* Engelm., is very similar to the coastal variety but is taller and more slender. It is native to mountainous regions from Alaska to Colorado. The Corsican Pine, *P. nigra* Arnold var. *maritima* Melville, is native to Corsica, Sicily and S. Italy. It is an erect, pyramidal evergreen tree up to 45 m high in Britain but higher in southern Europe, sparsely branched and developing a flat crown when old. Bark reddish-grey, flaky and shallowly fissured, on old trees dark grey

resolving into large longitudinal plates; leaves in pairs, rather sparse, slender and twisted, 12–18 cm long, and greyish-green; cones ovoid and pointed, 5–7.5 cm long. Introduced to Britain in 1759 where it is common as an amenity and forest tree. Useful for coastal areas and dune fixing, requires warm sunny summers to succeed. Timber has similar uses to Scots Pine. The Arolla Pine, *P. cembra* L., is native to the mountains of central Europe, and was introduced to Britain by the Duke of Argyll in 1746. It is an evergreen, erect, columnar, slow-growing tree, bearing short, stout branches and dense foliage from eye-level to the summit. Twigs covered in orange-brown down; leaves in groups of 5 tufted shoots, rough-edged and sharply pointed, 5–10 cm long, shiny green on outer side, greyish-green on inner side; cone ovoid, erect, 7.5–10 cm long, ripening from bluish-purple to shiny reddish-brown in second year. Cones do not open to shed seed, they fall to the ground whole and release the seeds when rotting or when broken up by foraging mammals or birds. The seeds are large and eaten by man. The timber, which is soft, fine grained and fragrant, is used in the manufacture of Swiss toys. Arolla Pine is grown to a limited extent for timber in Scandinavia.

Associated Macro-fungi
None specific in Britain. Many species associated with other pines are likely to be found.

Associated Insects
None specific in Britain. Many species associated with other pines are likely to be found.

General Information
Lodgepole stems were used by N. American Indians for their tepee supports; hence the common name.

Bark: Dark brown to black, resolving into small, rough, irregular, squarish plates.

Twigs: Young shoots greenish-brown and glabrous, then orange-brown, stout and twisted. Buds long-cylindrical, chestnut brown, resinous and twisted.

Leaves: Evergreen. In pairs, spreading or densely set, 4–10 cm long, rigid, often twisted. Dark green to paler green, never bluish-green.

Flowers: April–May. Monoecious, anemophilous. Male catkins abundant and clustered, yellow with pollen, about 2 cm long. Female conelet dark red, about 7 mm long.

Fruit: Almost sessile cone, borne on very young trees and thereafter throughout the tree's lifetime. Usually persistent for several years, in whorls of 2–5, ovoid-conical, often curved and pointing back down the shoots, 5 cm long, green ripening brown; scales at first minutely prickly.

A Bark, Coastal Lodgepole Pine.
B Young cones, Coastal Lodgepole Pine.
C Cones, Coastal Lodgepole Pine.

Taxodiaceae
Wellingtonia or Big Tree—*Sequoiadendron giganteum* (Lindl.) Buchholz

Wellingtonia

Coast
Redwood

Description
The open-grown Wellingtonia is an imposing and majestic tree. It is fairly rapid-growing, light-demanding, straight, windfirm and frost hardy. Narrowly conical in outline, the tree has a huge trunk which is very wide at the buttressed base, tapering gradually to the apex. The branches, which are comparatively light for such a tree, are downswept except for those near the summit, and all arch upwards at the tips. In California, their native home, there are known specimens up to 97 m high and 9 m in diameter: the largest, if not the tallest, trees in the world. Some are said to be over 3000 years old. The maximum height reached in Europe would appear to be about half that attained in California.

Timber
Sapwood yellowish-white, heartwood brownish-red, straight grained but coarse and knotty, very soft, exceedingly durable, non-shrinking and fairly strong. Useful for making tanks or vats due to resistance to acids; also constructional work, panelling, doors, weatherboards, shingles etc.

Range and Habitat
Native to Sierra Nevada, California. Introduced to Britain by William Lobb in 1853. Quite common as a parkland or amenity tree. Timber plantings very limited. Prefers deep moist soils in sheltered situations in areas with high rainfall. Does not like polluted air, and is subject to lightning strike.

Related Trees
The Coast Redwood, *Sequoia sempervirens* (D. Don) Endl., is native to coastal regions of California and Oregon and was introduced to Britain in the 19th century, where it is seen fairly frequently in parkland and arboreta. Said to be the tallest growing

tree in the world reaching 110 m; also very long-living and when felled will regenerate from the stump. Conical in outline, but usually not so pointed at apex as the Wellingtonia. The leaves on young shoots are scale-like; those on lateral twigs are Yew-like, set in two ranks on brown twigs. Growing requirements similar to Wellingtonia, but is not so hardy.

Associated Macro-fungi
None specific in Britain and Europe.

Associated Insects
None specific in Britain and Europe.

General Information
Wellingtonia is so named in honour of the Duke of Wellington. In America some specimen trees have been given names such as 'General Sherman', 'General Grant', and 'Grizzly Giant'. It is of good ornamental value in hilly areas but may seem obtrusive in flat countryside.

Bark: Can be 30–60 cm thick; rich brown or reddish, spongy, fibrous and scaly with broad, deep ridges.

Twigs: Young shoots are pale green and glabrous, minutely speckled with white. Buds without scales.

Leaves: Evergreen. Scale-like, alternate, each 4–12 mm long, lanceolate or ovate, concave with white speckles on upper surface, rounded and thickened on lower surface, crowded and covering shoots; pointed apices directed slightly outwards. Bluish-green to dark green. Odour of aniseed when crushed.

Flowers: Monoecious, anemophilous. Terminal on shoots and profuse on the tree. Male catkins very small, appear whitish in October, yellow with pollen in March or April. Female flowers ovoid, tiny, greenish-yellow, with keeled, pointed scales.

Fruit: Ovate-oblong cone, pendant on a long stalk, often bunched; each cone 7.5 cm long, ripening in second year from green to dark brown and remaining on the tree for many years.

A Bark, Wellingtonia.
B Young cones, Wellingtonia.
C Mature cones, Wellingtonia.

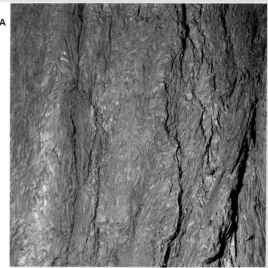

Cupressaceae
Monterey Cypress—*Cupressus macrocarpa* Hartw.

Monterey
Cypress

Description
The Monterey Cypress is a shade-tolerant, frost-tender, not windfirm, fairly fast-growing evergreen tree. In Britain it attains heights of 25 m or more with an outline that is at first conical, later becoming broad and flat-topped with a similar appearance to the Cedar of Lebanon. The branches are ascending, numerous and close-set on young trees. Its age limit in Europe has not yet been ascertained.

Timber
Sapwood and heartwood yellowish, spice-scented, close grained, fairly durable but only moderately strong. Inclined to be knotty; takes fine polish. Best timber suitable for joinery and furniture.

Range and Habitat
Native to a small coastal area of Monterey in California and the island of Guadeloupe. Introduced to Australia, New Zealand, southern Africa and S. America. Seeds sent to Europe in 1838. Planted as an amenity tree with varying degrees of success over much of Britain, in parks, gardens, cemeteries, and also close-planted for hedges. It only does well in mild, unexposed situations, but is tolerant of sea-laden winds and will thrive on most substrates.

Related Trees
Today the Monterey Cypress has been largely superseded in use by the Leyland Cypress, *Cupressocyparis leylandii* Dallim, which is a hybrid between *Cupressus macrocarpa* and *Chamaecyparis nootkatensis* Spach., combining the best characteristics of both parents. The Mexican Cypress, *Cupressus lusitanica* Mill., native to Mexico and Guatemala, was introduced to Britain at least three centuries ago, but is not very hardy there and is now rare. It is a conical, single-stemmed tree; bark shiny brown, often spiralled,

shallowly fissured vertically and forming peeling strips; foliage evenly set and drooping; scale-leaves with prominent points, little scent when crushed; cones small, globular, 1.5 cm in diameter, bloomed with bluish-grey, ripening shiny brown, scales with points. The Italian or Funeral Cypress, *Cupressus sempervirens* L., native to the Mediterranean area, is usually seen as a narrow, spire-like tree, attaining heights of 25–45 m and bearing short, fastigiate branches. It is extensively planted over most of temperate Europe, except Britain, where it is rarely seen. In Italy, Spain and Portugal nearly every cemetery has an avenue or grove of these trees, which, with their dark, sombre foliage have long been associated with death. Scale-leaves dull, dark green, very tiny and closely adpressed to the shoots; cones ovoid, lumpy, finally dull greyish. Timber pleasantly scented, strong, exceedingly durable; was very much in demand centuries ago and is still used for stakes, vine props and carvings.

Associated Macro-fungi
None specific in Britain.

Associated Insects
None specific in Britain.

General Information
Two Italian Cypresses planted by Michelangelo are said to be still living this century.

Bark: Dark reddish-brown, scaly and shallowly ridged; old trees with a whitish tinge.

Twigs: Straight, evenly set and almost parallel to each other; young shoots covered by scale-leaves borne evenly on four sides.

Leaves: Evergreen. Scale-like, closely overlapping each other, very small, 3 mm long, ovate, and blunt at apex. Dark green with paler margins. Lemon scented when crushed.

Flowers: March–June. Monoecious, anemophilous. Minute, terminal on separate branchlets. Male catkins ovoid, green then yellow with pollen. Female flowers oblong, consisting of 6–10 bright green, ovule-bearing scales.

Fruit: Globose, lumpy cone, 2.5–3.7 cm long, ripening green to glossy purplish-brown. Angled seeds are numerous under each scale.

A Bark, Monterey Cypress.
B Mature cones, Monterey Cypress.
C Bark, Mexican Cypress.
D Cones, leaves and ♂ flowers, Mexican Cypress.

Cupressaceae
Lawson Cypress or Port Orford Cedar—
Chamaecyparis lawsoniana (Murray) Parl.

Lawson
Cypress

Description
The Lawson Cypress is a false cypress with a narrowly conical outline, similar to that of Western Red Cedar, but with a drooping leading shoot. In America it reaches 60 m in height with boles of up to 2.5 m in diameter. In Britain, where it may not yet have attained its full height, there are trees 36 m high. The species is fast-growing, shade-tolerant, windfirm and exceedingly frost-hardy, even though scorching is fairly frequent.

Timber
European-grown is white to yellowish, with strong resinous scent, straight grained and fairly hard but light, exceedingly durable but not very strong. Insect repellant. American timber superior to European. Uses include battery separators, joinery, cupboard and wardrobe linings, clothes chests, sleepers, fencing posts etc.

Range and Habitat
Native to S.W. Oregon and N.W. California. Introduced to Britain in 1854 and named after Charles or Peter Lawson of Edinburgh. Very common in Britain and Europe as an amenity tree along with the remarkably numerous and varied cultivars, mainly propagated by cuttings. Not conservative as to substrate and will thrive on most soils if not too heavy or wet. Does best on rich loam in sheltered situations, with a high annual rainfall.

Related Trees
The Nootka Cypress, *C. nootkatensis* Spach., is a very hardy tree, native in America from Alaska to northern Oregon, usually single-stemmed, very very regular in outline, narrowly conic and up to 30 m high in Britain. The lower branches are heavy and upturned, the higher branches lighter and slightly ascending. The bark, in various shades

of brown, is fissured vertically and scaly. The foliage is pendulous and fern-like, dull green above, paler beneath. The scale-leaves are pointed and even in length. Crushed foliage smells rank and oily. Ripe cones are globular, dull brown, about 1 cm in diameter, each scale bearing a large spine at its end. A beautiful tree frequently planted as an ornamental in parks and large gardens. The Hinoki Cypress, *C. obtusa* (Sieb. & Zucc.) Endl., is a native of Japan, introduced to Britain in 1861 and seen fairly frequently as an ornamental in western parts of the country. Grows up to 40 m in height, but there are several cultivars of smaller dimensions. The scale-leaves are small and blunt, and the crushed foliage has a resinous scent reminiscent of eucalyptus.

Associated Macro-fungi
None specific in Britain and Europe.

Associated Insects
None specific in Britain and Europe.

General Information
It is said that in America, men working with this timber in sawmills tend to suffer from kidney trouble. Foliage used by florists for wreaths and backing. Makes good hedge material although inferior to Western Red Cedar for this.

Bark: Young trees smooth and brownish-green; later greyish-brown, resolving into longitudinal shaggy plates, and fissured.

Twigs: Regularly set in flattened sprays, hidden by scale-leaves; bare older twigs are dull brown or purplish.

Leaves: Evergreen. Scale-like, adpressed to the shoots in opposite pairs, pointed at apex, only 2–4 mm long. Bluish-green or dark green, those on upper side have a translucent gland in centre,

those below are minutely streaked with white. Crushed foliage has odour of parsley.

Flowers: March–April. Monoecious, anemophilous. Terminal on branchlets, minute. Male catkins cylindrical, bright crimson, and profuse. Female flowers whorls of small, acute, green bract-scales.

Fruit: Globular, pea-sized cone, ripening green to pale greyish-brown in October, numerous and persistent. Seeds slightly winged.

A Bark, Lawson Cypress.
B Leaves and ♀ cones, Lawson Cypress.
C Old cones and ♂ flowers, Lawson Cypress.

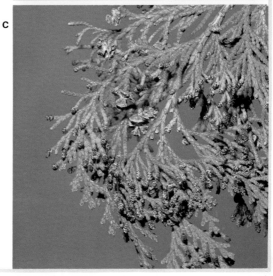

Cupressaceae
Western Red Cedar—*Thuja plicata* D. Don ex Lamb

Western Red
Cedar

Description
The Western Red Cedar is a most beautiful, formidable, rapid-growing, rootfirm and hardy tree. It is conical in outline and typically single-stemmed with a buttressed base and fluted bole, bearing an erect main leader and fern-like foliage. In N. America it attains a height of 60 m with trunk diameters varying between 1 and 2.5 m, and may live for 800 years. Trees introduced into Britain in 1853 are 38 m high and still thriving.

Timber
Variable in quality according to climate and situation. Sapwood yellow, heartwood darker and reddish. Weathered timber becomes grey or silvery-grey. Very soft, straight grained, somewhat coarse in texture, very light in weight and not very strong. Said to be immune to *Serpula lacrymans* (Fries) Karst., the Dry Rot Fungus. Heartwood very durable, sapwood not at all. The timber is much in demand and uses include weatherboards, roofing shingles, greenhouses, fencing, telegraph poles, barrels, boats, gates, interior decoration etc.

Range and Habitat
Indigenous to western N. America from Alaska to California, where it is an important timber tree. Found throughout Europe as an introduced park, garden or timber tree; brought to Britain by William Lobb in 1853. Prefers a deep fertile loom in sheltered areas and a moist atmosphere, but is not too conservative in these respects; thriving at high elevations, in exposed situations, and is tolerant of highly alkaline substrates. Windfirm, frost hardy and shade tolerant.

Related Trees
The Eastern White Cedar or American Arborvitae, *T. occidentalis* L., native to eastern N. America and introduced to Britain in 1596, is a slower growing, shorter living and smaller tree than Western Red Cedar. Foliage pale yellowish-green on underside and apple-scented; cone-scales have small spine at tips. There are several dwarf cultivars which are commonly planted in gardens. The Chinese Thuja, *T. orientalis* L., native to China and Korea, was introduced to Britain in 1752. It is a small tree with dense erect branches, and underside of foliage is uniformly dark green; not scented. There are several cultivars in existence.

Associated Macro-fungi
None specific in Britain and Europe.

Associated Insects
None specific in Britain and Europe.

General Information
The American trees are often referred to as Arborvitae, meaning 'tree of life'. The fresh foliage is used by florists in wreaths and other floral arrangements. Certain tribes of N. American Indians made their totem poles and canoes from the wood. Not good for wildlife but very useful for hedging.

Bark: Dark reddish-brown, fibrous and thick; older trees have irregular thick ridges which tend to lift and break away from the trunk.

Twigs: Young shoots are covered by scale-leaves and are hidden from view, when they are shed the twigs are seen to be reddish-brown; they feel swollen and hard at the extremities.

Leaves: Evergreen. Scale-like, adpressed to shoots except at apices, in opposite pairs in 4 ranks. Each leaf 3 mm long, obovate and blunt. Glossy green above, paler beneath with silvery white markings. Odour of pineapple; eventually they fade to brown and are shed.

Flowers: March–April. Monoecious, anemophilous. Male catkins terminal on young shoots, minute, 2 mm long; dark

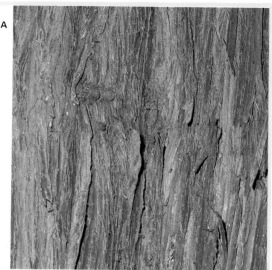

red, then yellow with pollen. Female flowers solitary on small branchlets, similar in size to males, bud-like and light green.

Fruit: Small cone up to 2 cm long, erect or semi-erect, with 10–12 slender overlapping scales united only at the base, green at first then pale yellow, ripening brown in autumn. Winged seeds in pairs at base of scales which are not spiny.

A Bark, Western Red Cedar.
B Young cones, Western Red Cedar.
C Mature cones, Western Red Cedar.

Cupressaceae
Common Juniper—*Juniperus communis* L.

Common
Juniper

Description
The Common Juniper is a very slow-growing, many-branched, untidy, spreading, evergreen shrub, 0.5–1.5 m high, or a small tree up to 6 m high and columnar in outline. It is a very variable species, its form and size being considerably affected by its location.

Timber
Aromatic. Sapwood white, heartwood red when cut, quickly becoming brown. Very knotty and hard with irregular grain, exceedingly durable, fairly strong, and insect resistant. The small amount available is useful for cupboard linings, pencils and other small articles.

Range and Habitat
Native to Europe, S.W. Asia, and N. America, probably has a wider distribution in the northern hemisphere than any other tree or shrub. Once common in many parts of the British Isles on dryish neutral and alkaline substrates. Due to intensive farming, burning, and land reclamation, Juniper has lost a lot of ground in Britain and is now locally common only on the chalk of S. England, parts of Wales, northern England, Scotland, and western Ireland.

Related Trees
J. communis var. *nana* is a prostrate northern form with more crowded, shorter, and often blunt leaves. Junipers of many species and varieties are suitable for garden planting and ground cover. Amongst the most popular are Chinese Juniper, *J. chinensis* L., Pencil Cedar, *J. virginiana* L., and Creeping Savin, *J. sabina* L., which has a strong, disagreeable odour and biting taste, and is native to the mountainous regions of central and southern Europe.

Associated Macro-fungi
None known to be specific.

Associated Insects
Lepidoptera—Moths: *Thera cognata*

Thunb., Chestnut-coloured Carpet; *T. juniperata* L., Juniper Carpet, larvae on leaves. *Eupithecia pusillata* Denis & Schiff., Juniper Pug. Micro-Moths: *Aethes rutilana* Hübn., larvae in tubular webs amongst needles. *Dichomeris marginella* F.; *D. juniperella* L., larvae in web amongst needles. *Argyresthia arceuthina* Zell., larvae in shoots; *A. praecocella* Zell., larvae in berries; *A. dilectella* Zell., larvae in shoots; *A. aurulentella* Staint.; *A. abdominalis* Zell., larvae in leaves. **Coleoptera**—Weevils: *Polydrusus marginatus* Steph.; *Apion pomonae* F. **Homoptera**—Scale insects: *Carulaspis juniperi* Bouché, causes juniper scale. **Hymenoptera**—Sawflies: *Monoctenus juniperi* L., apparently confined to the Spey Valley in Britain, but also occurs in N. and central Europe. **Diptera**—Gall midges: *Schmidtiella gemmarum* Rübs., leaves distorted with elongated gall. *Oligotrophus juniperinus* L.; *O. schmidti* Rübs.; *O. panteli* Kief., along with other species of the genus, in gall formed by cluster of needles at tip of shoot; each gall contains one larva.

General Information
Country people used to kindle their fires with the highly inflammable foliage. The fruits are used to flavour certain foodstuffs, including game meats and gin, and to cure some foods. They are also distilled to make oil of juniper. Dirk handles were made from the wood. The tree under which the Prophet Elijah rested whilst fleeing from Jezebel is said to have been a juniper.

Bark: Reddish-brown, fibrous and flaking.

Twigs: Reddish-brown to dark brown. Buds minute and brown.

Leaves: Evergreen. Sessile, in whorls of 3, about 2 cm long, rigid, sharply pointed with thickened margins, awl-shaped at right-angles to the stem. Green with broad white band above,

wholly green beneath. Crushed or bruised foliage is aromatically fragrant.

Flowers: May. Usually dioecious. Males axillary, bud-like and in whorls of 3, stamens numerous, pale yellow. Female flowers axillary, minute, bud-like and green with fleshy scales.

Fruit: Ripen September–October of second year, small and globular. A berry-like cone, green then bluish, finally blue-black with a white bloom. Very fleshy and pungent, 3-seeded, empty scales at base. Dispersed by birds.

A Habit, Common Juniper.
B Cones, Common Juniper.
C Berries, Common Juniper.

Glossary

Acicular—See leaf shapes, p. 13.

Acuminate—See leaf shapes, p. 13.

Acute—See leaf shapes, p. 13.

Adpressed—Lying close and flat against.

Anemophilous—Pollinated by wind.

Anther—Upper part of the stamen which bears the pollen sacs.

Aril—Fleshy covering, surrounding or partly surrounding the seeds of certain plants.

Attenuate—See leaf shapes, p. 13.

Auricle—Small ear-like projection.

Axil—Upper angle between leaf and the stem bearing it.

Bisexual (flowers)—Having ovary and stamens in one flower.

Bracteole—Small bract between the normal bract and the individual flower.

Compound (leaf)—Completely divided into a number of separate leaflets.

Caducous—Falling very early.

Calyx—Collective name for sepals.

Campanulate—Bell-shaped.

Clone—A plant produced asexually from a single parent, and therefore possessing all the characters of that parent.

Coppiced—Regularly and periodically cut to ground level before mature.

Cordate—Heart-shaped. See leaf shapes, p.13.

Corolla—Collective name for petals.

Corymb—Raceme in which the lengths of the flower stalks are such that all the flowers are at the same level and form a flat head.

Cultivar—Variety preserved by cultivation.

Cupule—Cup-shaped growth enclosing fruit and formed by a number of bracts.

Crenate—See leaf shapes, p. 13.

Cyme—Inflorescence in which each flower is terminal on the stem and the second flower grows from an axillary bud on the stem of the first. Cymes can be two sided if a pair of buds develop on the stem of the first.

Deciduous (trees)—Leaves are shed at the onset of winter.

Dentate—Toothed. See leaf shapes, p. 13.

Dichotomous—Growth of stem forks because growth is continued from a pair of axillary buds, usually due to the terminal bud producing a flower.

Dioecious—Male and female flowers on separate plants.

Drupe—Fruit in which the outer part of the ovary wall becomes fleshy whilst the inner layer forms a hard stone around the seed(s).

Elliptic—See leaf shapes, p. 13.

Entire—See leaf shapes, p. 13.

Entomophilous—Pollinated by insects.

Esculent—Edible.

Exstipulate—Without stipules.

Fastigiate—Branches erect and close together.

Fluted (tree trunk)—With vertical rounded grooves.

Fusiform—Spindle shaped.

Glabrous—No hairs present.

Globose—Almost globular.

Glutinous—Sticky.

Imparipinnate (leaf)—Leaflets arranged in pairs with an odd terminal leaflet.

Infundibuliform—Funnel-shaped.

Involucre—Whorl of bracts surrounding a flower or flower cluster.

Lacerate—Deeply and irregularly divided.

Lanceolate—See leaf shapes, p. 13.

Lenticel—Breathing pores in the bark.

Lignicolous—On or attached to wood.

Linear—See leaf shapes, p. 13.

Monadelphous—Stamens united by their filaments.

Monoecious—Male and female flowers on the same plant.

Node—Region of the stem from which leaf or leaves arise.

Oblong—See leaf shapes, p. 13.

Obovate—See leaf shapes, p. 13.

Ovate—See leaf shapes, p. 13.

Ovule—The structure containing the egg cell and which after fertilisation becomes the seed.

Palmate—See leaf shapes, p. 13.

Panicle—Branching raceme.

Papilionaceous—Butterfly shaped.

Peduncle—Stalk of an inflorescence.

Perfect (flowers)—Bisexual (q.v.).

Perianth—Collective name for petals and sepals.

Petiole—Leaf stalk.

Pinnate (leaf)—Leaflets carried on both sides of a leaf stalk. See leaf shapes, p. 13.

Pistil—Female part of the flower which consists of the ovary, style, and stigma.

Pollarded—Lopped a few feet above the ground to encourage the formation of many young branches.

Polyphagous (insects)—Feeding on many species of plants.

Pome—Fruit in which the end of the flower stem (receptacle) becomes fused with the wall of the fruit and provides a fleshy covering to the fruit (e.g. apple).

Protandrous—Stamens shed pollen before the pistil is mature.

Protogynous—Pistil is mature and receptive to pollen before stamens shed their pollen.

Pubescent—Covered with soft hairs.

Raceme—Inflorescence in which all the flowers grow from axillary buds on the main stem and therefore the oldest flowers are lower on the stem.

Samara—Flat, winged seed vessel.

Serrate—See leaf shapes, p. 13.

Sessile—Stalkless.

Simple (leaf)—Single blade or lamina.

Sinuate—See leaf shapes, p. 13.

Stamen—Male bearing organ of the flower consisting of anther and filament or stalk.

Stigma—Part of the pistil that is receptive to pollen.

Stipule—Leaf-like outgrowth at the base of leaf; stipules occur in pairs.

Style—Extension of the ovary that carries the stigma.

Ternate (leaf)—Compound with three leaflets.

Tomentose—With dense, woolly pubescence.

Transluscent—Transmitting some light.

Truncate—See leaf shapes, p. 13.

Umbo—Raised centre of a cone-scale.

Vascular—Containing woody tissue.

Bibliography

BENSON, R. B. *Handb. Ident. British Insects* (3 parts), Vol. 6 (Part 2). Royal Ent. Soc. London, 1951, 1952, 1958.

BOULTON, E. H. B. and JAY, B. A. *British Timbers*. A. & C. Black, London, 1944.

CHRYSTAL, R. N. *Insects of the British Woodlands*. F. Warne, London, 1937.

DARLINGTON, A. *The Pocket Encyclopaedia of Plant Galls*. Blandford Press, London, 1968.

EADY, R. D. and QUINLAN, J. *Handb. Ident. British Insects*, Vol. 8 (Part 1). Royal Ent. Soc. London, 1963.

EDLIN, H. L. *What Wood is That?* Thames & Hudson, London, 1969.

EDLIN, H. L. *Collins Guide to Tree Planting & Cultivation*. Collins, London, 1970.

EDLIN, H. L. *The Observer's Book of Trees*. F. Warne, London, 1975.

EMMET, A. M. (ed.) *A Field Guide to the Smaller British Lepidoptera*. British Ent. and Nat. Hist. Society, London (not dated).

HART, C. E. and RAYMOND, C. *British Trees in Colour*. Michael Joseph, London, 1974.

HERING, E. M. *Bestimmungstabellen der Blattminen von Europa*, 3 vols. Junk, Den Haag.

HODGKINSON, I. D. and WHITE, I. M. *Handb. Ident. British Insects* (Aphididae part), Vol. 2 (Part 4). Royal Ent. Soc. London, 1979.

HOWARTH, T. G. *South's British Butterflies*. F. Warne, London, 1973.

JOHNS, Rev. C. A. *British Trees and Shrubs*. Routledge & Kegan Paul, London.

JOY, N. H. *A Practical Handbook of British Beetles* (2 vols). E. W. Classey, Oxon, 1932 (reprint 1976).

KEY, HAZEL. *Ivies*. Wisley Handbook 34. Royal Horticultural Society, 1978.

KLOET, G. S. and HINCKS, W. D. A Check List of British Insects (revised). In *Handb. Ident. British Insects*, Vol. 11 (parts 1–5). Royal Ent. Soc. London, 1964, 1972, 1975, 1977, 1978.

LANGE, M. and HORA, F. B. *Collins Guide to Mushrooms and Toadstools*. Collins, London, 1963.

LE QUESNE, W. J. Hemiptera (Homoptera) (2 parts). *Handb. Ident. British Insects* Vol. 2 (Part 2). Royal Ent. Soc. London, 1965, 1969.

LORENZ, H. and KRAUS, M. *Die Larvalsystematik der Blattwespen*. Berlin, 1957.

MITCHELL, ALAN. *A Field Guide to the Trees of Britain & Northern Europe*. Collins, London, 1974.

NICHOLSON, B. E. and CLAPHAM, A. R. *The Oxford Book of Trees*. Oxford University Press, Oxford, 1975.

PHILLIPS, ROGER. *Trees in Britain*. Pan Books, London, 1978.

POLUNIN, OLEG. *Trees and Bushes of Britain & Europe*. Oxford University Press, Oxford, 1975.

ROSS, H. and HEDICKE, H. *Die Pflanzengallen Mittel und Nordeuropas*. Fischer, Jena, 1927.

SOOTHILL, E. and FAIRHURST, A. *The New Field Guide to Fungi*. Michael Joseph, London, 1978.

SOUTH, R. (ed. Edelsten, H. M., Fletcher, D. S. and Collins, R. J.). *The Moths of the British Isles* (2 vols). F. Warne, London, 1961.

STROYAN, H. L. G. Homoptera (Aphididae part). *Handb. Ident. British Insects*, Vol. 2 (Part 4). Royal Ent. Soc. London, 1977.

WALSH, G. B. and DIBB, J. R. *A Coleopterist's Handbook*. Journal Amateur Entomologists Society, Vol. 11. London, 1954.

WATLING, ROY. *Identification of the Larger Fungi*. Hulton Educational, Amersham, 1973.

Index of Trees—English Names

Index of Trees—Latin Names

Index of Fungi

Index of Insects